PRELIS 2:
User's Reference Guide

- explores data
- does basic correlational output
- polychoric corr.
- weight matrix

PRELIS™ 2

User's Reference Guide

A program for multivariate data screening and data summarization; a preprocessor for LISREL

Karl G. Jöreskog and Dag Sörbom

Uppsala University

Published by:

Scientific Software International, Inc.
7383 N. Lincoln Avenue, Suite 100
Chicago, IL 60646–1704
Tel: (847) 675–0720
Fax: (847) 675–2140
URL: http://www.ssicentral.com

ISBN: 0–89498–041–6

Note from the editor on the third edition

The PRELIS user's guide was first published in 1986. A second edition appeared in 1988. In 1993, SSI published a major upgrade of the program: PRELIS 2.

The authors, Prof. Karl G. Jöreskog and Prof. Dag Sörbom, described the improvements that were made in two documents: *New features in PRELIS 2* and *Simulation with PRELIS 2 and LISREL 8*. SSI published these two documents as inserts together with the original PRELIS user's guide as the temporary *PRELIS 2 User's Reference Guide*. Meanwhile, the authors have undertaken a complete rewrite of the LISREL 8 and PRELIS 2 documentation.

Because this task is taking longer than anticipated, SSI sought and received permission from the authors to integrate those three separate pieces into one document, thereby creating a more accessible product for the user of the program, without making substantive changes to the text.

Chapters 2 and 3 have been updated and now describe the current state of the program. Commands, keywords and options that have become obsolete with PRELIS 2 have been deleted and the new commands, keywords and options added.

The former inserts are now appendixes (B, C, and D), resulting in one index and one list of references for the PRELIS 2 documentation.

The methodological background for the program together with the examples is still spread out over different parts: Chapter 1 has the old PRELIS text, while Appendix B and Appendix C describe the improvements and new features. The new examples can also be found in those appendixes; the PRELIS 1 examples — still very useful — are in Chapter 4.

At the same time, the whole documentation has been redone with the LaTeX computer typesetting system so that it now conforms with the other LISREL documentation.

The complete LISREL documentation now consists of five manuals.

> *PRELIS 2: User's Reference Guide*
> *LISREL 8: User's Reference Guide*
> *LISREL 8: Structural Equation Modeling with the SIMPLIS Command Language*
> *LISREL 8: New Statistical Features*
> *Interactive LISREL: User's Guide*

All manuals are available from SSI.

The last manual applies to the Windows version of the program. It describes in detail the user interface that comes with the program on that platform. SSI offers a free student edition of Interactive LISREL on its website.

The other four manuals are platform independent and may be used for all operating systems that the program is available for.

Those manuals introduce the reader to the methodology of structural equation modeling, both theoretically and through a variety of applications. The present manual, *PRELIS 2: User's Reference Guide*, discusses the intricacies of multivariate data screening and preparing the data for subsequent model fitting. The *LISREL 8: User's Reference Guide* elaborates on the fitting and testing of structural equation models with the use of the *LISREL* syntax, while *LISREL 8: Structural Equation Modeling with the SIMPLIS Command Language* does the same with the *SIMPLIS* syntax. *LISREL 8: New Statistical Features* describes all the statistical analysis tools that were added to version 8.30 of the program: multilevel analysis, two-stage least-squares estimation, exploratory factor analysis, principal components, normal scores, and latent variable scores.

Chicago, February 1999.

Preface

PRELIS is a preprocessor for LISREL. But it can also be conveniently used to provide a first descriptive look at raw data even when no LISREL analysis is intended or when further analysis will be done by other programs.

Experience in consultation with users of LISREL has shown that they are not always sufficiently familiar with characteristics and problems of their raw data when they set out to estimate and test a LISREL model. Problems in the raw data can often account for peculiarities that occur when estimating and testing LISREL models.

PRELIS does a fair amount of data screening, and has been prepared in the spirit of Tukey's (1977) principle: "It is important to understand what you *can do* before you learn to measure how *well* you seem to have *done* it."

PRELIS can read raw data on continuous, censored, and ordinal variables. It can transform variables in various ways and it can compute many different measures of association between pairs of such variables. In some cases, PRELIS can provide an estimate of the asymptotic (large sample) covariance matrix of such measures. These can be used in LISREL to perform a more accurate and powerful analysis than has been available with previous versions of LISREL.

PRELIS has been carefully tested. We describe all the functions and options of the program as accurately as possible in this user's guide. Minor errors may remain undetected in the program or the user's guide, for which we take full responsibility.

Karl G. Jöreskog and Dag Sörbom   June 1986

Contents

List of tables

List of examples
(with input and data files)

This book has many examples illustrating most of the common types of analyses used with PRELIS and LISREL. For beginners of LISREL it is instructive to go over these examples to learn how to set up the command file for particular problems. We also suggest using these examples as exercises in the following ways:

- ❏ Compare correlations obtained with different specifications: KM, OM, PM, etc.
- ❏ Use the different transformations available and study the change in distribution characteristics.
- ❏ Study the effect of declaring different scale types for the same variables.
- ❏ Request other options for the output.
- ❏ Make deliberate mistakes in the input file and see what happens.

Input and data files for these examples are included with the program on the distribution media. For these files we use the following naming conventions.

The first part in the filename refers to the example in the book. Thus, EX2B means Example 2B. Command files have the suffix LS8 for LISREL 8 files and PR2 for PRELIS 2 files. Generally, the suffix after the period in the name of a data file refers to the type of data it contains:

- ☐ LAB for labels
- ☐ RAW for raw data
- ☐ DAT for a file containing several types of data

Example 1A through Example 6C are basic PRELIS examples, as described in Chapter 4. Example 7A through Example 11 deal with the new features of PRELIS 2, as described in Appendix B. The remaining examples can be found in Appendix C *Simulation with PRELIS 2 and LISREL 8*. They combine PRELIS and LISREL input files and demonstrate the interplay between the two programs.

1

PRELIS procedures

Users of LISREL need to know the characteristics of their data well, so they can avoid any problems that might arise. To help LISREL users become aware of these problems and avoid mistakes, a new program, PRELIS, has been developed.

It is particularly important to know the scale type of each variable, the distribution of each variable, the distribution of the variables jointly, and the distribution of missing values over variables and cases.

When some or all of the variables are ordinal or censored, it is essential to choose the right type of correlations to analyze. Failure to do so can lead to considerable bias in estimated LISREL parameters and other quantities. PRELIS can help with these considerations and with others summarized briefly below and described in detail on the following pages.

1.1 Data

PRELIS reads raw data of any numeric form from an external file, case after case. As the data are not stored in active memory,[1] the number of cases (the sample size) is limited only by the amount of available storage space on tape or disk.

PRELIS can read grouped data and patterned data where each case carries a weight.

PRELIS does a fair amount of data screening and can compute many kinds of correlations and other moments for ordinal and censored variables.

---

[1]PRELIS 2 now stores the data matrix in memory, if possible (see page 144).

For LISREL users who need to explore the data further before a suitable LISREL model can be specified, PRELIS estimates the regression of any variable on any other variables.

The program can be used to take a first quick look at data from questionnaires in surveys.

1.2 Variables

A numeric value may be defined for each variable to represent a missing value. Such a numeric value can also be defined collectively for a group of variables or globally for all variables.

The scale type of each variable may be declared as ordinal, censored (see page 5), or continuous.[2] Groups of variables (including all variables) of the same scale type may be declared collectively. Ordinal variables may have up to 15 categories.

The program can estimate correlations between censored variables and ordinal or continuous variables.

Continuous variables may be transformed using any one of a large family of transformations. Ordinal variables may be recoded or transformed to normal scores, or they may first be recoded and then transformed to normal scores. Maximum and/or minimum values of censored variables may be transformed to normal scores.

PRELIS can compute Mardia's measure of relative multivariate kurtosis.

1.3 Correlations

PRELIS replaces that part of LISREL 6 which computes polychoric and polyserial correlations, and it does them much better, much faster, and with more informative output.

---

[2]PRELIS 2 now offers the selection of *fixed* variables, see pages 146 and 178.

1 PRELIS PROCEDURES

PRELIS computes six different types of correlation coefficients: product-moment (Pearson) correlations based on raw scores, product-moment correlations based on normal or optimal scores, canonical, polychoric (including tetrachoric), and polyserial (including biserial).[3]

For each polychoric or polyserial correlation, the program provides a test of the model underlying the computation of this correlation.

PRELIS can compute estimates of the asymptotic variances and covariances of estimated product-moment correlations, polychoric correlations, and polyserial correlations. These can be used with WLS (Weighted Least Squares) in LISREL.

1.4 Matrices

PRELIS computes the appropriate moment matrix (moment matrix about zero, covariance matrix, or correlation matrix) for input to LISREL, depending on the type of variables in the data.

Moment matrices may be computed using either pairwise deletion or listwise deletion.

PRELIS produces an estimate of the asymptotic (large sample) covariance matrix of the estimated sample variances and covariances under arbitrary non-normal distributions (see Browne, 1982, 1984). This can be used to compute a weight matrix for WLS (Weighted Least Squares, equivalent to Browne's ADF) in LISREL.

PRELIS may be used to compute a diagonal matrix consisting of estimates of the asymptotic variances of estimated variances, covariances, or correlations. These diagonal matrices can be used with DWLS (diagonally weighted least squares) in LISREL.

1.5 Output

PRELIS printed output is compact, yet it contains detailed information about all univariate and bivariate sample distributions.

---

[3]With PRELIS 2, Spearman rank correlations and Kendall's tau-c correlations are also available, see page 167

The program writes the requested moment matrix onto a file that can be read directly by LISREL. Requested asymptotic covariance matrices may also be saved in files that can be read directly by LISREL 7.

1.6   Three types of variables

PRELIS can deal with three types of variables: continuous, ordinal, and censored.

Continuous variable

Observations are assumed to come from an interval or a ratio scale and to have metric properties. Means, variances, and higher moments of these variables will be computed in the usual way.

Ordinal variable

Observations are assumed to represent responses to a set of ordered categories, such as a five-category Likert scale. Here, it is only assumed that a person who responds in one category has more of a characteristic than a person who responds in a lower category. For each ordinal variable x, it is assumed that there is a latent continuous variable ξ that is normally distributed with mean zero and unit variance. The assumption of normality is not testable given only x; but for each pair of variables where x is involved, PRELIS attempts a test of the assumption of bivariate normality.

Assuming that there are k categories on x, we write $x = i$ to mean that x belongs to category i. The actual score values in the data may be arbitrary and are irrelevant as long as the ordinal information is retained. That is, low scores correspond to low-order categories of x that are associated with smaller values of ξ, and high scores correspond to high-order categories that are associated with larger values of ξ.

The connection between x and ξ is that $x = \xi$ is equivalent to $\alpha_{i-1} < \xi \leq \alpha_i$, where $\alpha_0 = -\infty$, $\alpha_1 < \alpha_2 < \cdots < \alpha_{k-1}$, and $\alpha_k = +\infty$ are parameters called threshold values. If there are k categories, there are $k - 1$ unknown thresholds.

Censored variable

Variable x represents a latent variable ξ observed on an interval scale above a threshold value A. Below A, the value $x = A$ is observed:

$$x = \xi \quad \text{if} \quad \xi > A ,$$

$$x = A \quad \text{if} \quad \xi \leq A .$$

The value A is known and is equal to the smallest observed value of x. The latent variable ξ is assumed to be normally distributed with unknown mean μ and standard deviation σ, which are estimated by the maximum-likelihood method.

The censored variable just defined will be said to be *censored below*. PRELIS can also deal with variables that are *censored above*:

$$x = \xi \quad \text{if} \quad \xi < B ,$$

$$x = B \quad \text{if} \quad \xi \geq B .$$

Variables that are censored *both above and below* are also handled by PRELIS.

Censored variables have a high concentration of cases at the lower or upper end of the distribution. The classical example of this is in Tobit analysis where, for example, $x =$ the price of an automobile purchased in the last year, with $x = 0$ if no car was purchased. Here ξ may represent a propensity to consume capital goods. Other examples may be $x =$ number of crimes committed or $x =$ number of days unemployed. Test scores that have a "floor" or a "ceiling" (a large proportion of cases with no items or with all items correct) are censored variables. Attitude questions where a large fraction of the population is expected to have the lowest or highest score or category may also be considered censored variables.

A key concept in the way PRELIS treats ordinal and censored variables is the use of normal scores.

For an ordinal variable, let n_j be the number of cases in the jth category. The threshold values are estimated from the (marginal) distribution of each variable as

$$\hat{\alpha}_i = \Phi^{-1}\left(\sum_{j=1}^{i} n_j/N\right) \qquad i = 1,\, 2,\, \ldots,\, k-1$$

where Φ^{-1} is the inverse standard normal distribution function, and N is the total number of real observations on the ordinal variable.

The *normal score* z_i corresponding to $x = i$ is the mean of ξ in the interval $\alpha_{i-1} < \xi \leq \alpha_i$, which is (see Johnson & Kotz, 1970, pp. 81–82)

$$z_i = \frac{\phi(\alpha_{i-1}) - \phi(\alpha_i)}{\Phi(\alpha_i) - \Phi(\alpha_{i-1})}$$

where ϕ and Φ are the standard normal density and distribution function, respectively. This normal score can be estimated as:

$$\hat{z}_i = (N/n_i)[\phi(\hat{\alpha}_{i-1}) - \phi(\hat{\alpha}_i)]$$

As can be readily verified, the weighted mean of the normal scores is 0.

For a variable censored below A, PRELIS uses the normal score associated with the interval $\xi \leq A$, which is

$$\hat{z}_A = \hat{\mu} - \frac{\phi[(A - \hat{\mu})/\hat{\sigma}]}{\Phi[(A - \hat{\mu})/\hat{\sigma}]}\hat{\sigma}$$

where $\hat{\mu}$ and $\hat{\sigma}$ are the maximum likelihood estimates of μ and σ.

For a variable censored above B, the normal score associated with the interval $\xi \geq B$ is:

$$\hat{z}_B = \hat{\mu} + \frac{\phi[(B - \hat{\mu})/\hat{\sigma}]}{\Phi[(B - \hat{\mu})/\hat{\sigma}]}\hat{\sigma}$$

1.7   Choosing the type of correlation matrix to analyze

When one or more of the variables to be analyzed in LISREL are ordinal, it is important to choose the right type of moment matrix to analyze. Because ordinal variables do not have an origin or unit of measurement, the only meaningful moment matrices, when all variables are ordinal, are correlation matrices. PRELIS provides four choices:

◻ KM (continuous).

A matrix of product-moment (Pearson) correlations based on raw scores; that is, with scores 1, 2, 3, ... on ordinal variables treated as if they come from interval-scaled variables. This is the KM option in PRELIS when *all* variables are declared *continuous*.

◻ KM (ordinal).

A matrix of product-moment (Pearson) correlations with observations on ordinal variables replaced by normal scores determined from the marginal distributions. This is the KM option in PRELIS when *ordinal* variables are *normalized*.

◻ OM

A matrix of product-moment (Pearson) correlations with observations on ordinal variables replaced by optimal scores determined for each pair. This is the OM option in PRELIS when *ordinal* variables are declared *ordinal*.

◻ PM

A matrix of polychoric correlations. This is the PM option in PRELIS when *ordinal* variables are declared *ordinal*.

To investigate which of these correlations is "best", we conducted two small experiments. The first involved only ordinal variables; the second involved both ordinal and continuous variables. These experiments included two correlations — Spearman's rank correlation and Kendall's tau-b — that are not included as options in PRELIS because of their poor results in the study.[4]

---

[4]PRELIS 2 now includes those correlations; see page 167 in Appendix B.

1.8 A Monte Carlo study of six correlation measures for ordinal variables

Let x and y be two ordinal variables with r and s categories, respectively. The Monte Carlo study involves five steps.

Step 1

Choose the population correlation ρ and threshold $\alpha_1, \alpha_2, \ldots, \alpha_{r-1}$ for x and $\beta_1, \beta_2, \ldots, \beta_{s-1}$ ($\alpha_0 = \beta_0 = -\infty$; $\alpha_r = \beta_s = +\infty$). Compute probabilities $\pi_{ij} = \Pr(x = i, y = j)$ as

$$\pi_{ij} = \int_{\alpha_{i-1}}^{\alpha_i} \int_{\beta_{j-1}}^{\beta_j} \phi_2(u, v) \, du \, dv$$

where ϕ_2 is the standard bivariate normal density with correlation ρ.

Step 2

Generate a random observation $x = i$, $y = j$ with probability π_{ij}. Repeat this N times. This gives a contingency table:

$$\begin{bmatrix} n_{11} & n_{12} & \cdots & n_{1s} \\ n_{21} & n_{22} & \cdots & n_{2s} \\ \vdots & \vdots & \ddots & \vdots \\ n_{r1} & n_{r2} & \cdots & n_{rs} \end{bmatrix}$$

Step 3

Compute all six correlation estimates and score 1 for the estimate closest to ρ. The six correlation types are:

KM (continuous)	PMC-RS	Product-moment correlation (raw scores)
⋆	SPEARMAN	Spearman's rank correlation
⋆	KENDALL	Kendall's tau-b coefficient
OM	CANON	Canonical correlation
KM (ordinal)	PMC-NS	Product-moment correlation (normal scores)
PM	POLYCHOR	Polychoric correlation

⋆ Spearman's rank correlation and Kendall's tau-b coefficient were at first not included in PRELIS because of the poor result obtained for these correlations. However, PRELIS 2 now computes these correlations.

The correlation measures PMC-RS, PMC-NS, CANON, and POLYCHOR correspond to the four PRELIS options KM (continuous), KM (ordinal), OM, and PM, respectively. All six correlations can be computed from the contingency table. The first five of these correspond to some sort of scoring system for the categories and the product-moment correlation computed for this scoring system. For example, the canonical correlation chooses scores for the categories that will maximize the correlation. The polychoric correlation, on the other hand, is not a correlation between two sets of scores but is, rather, an estimate of the correlation in the latent bivariate normal distribution representing the two ordinal variables.

Step 4

Repeat Steps 2 and 3 three hundred times.

Step 5

Compute the mean, variance, bias, and mean squared error.

Some typical results

Results from two populations are presented in Tables 1.1 and 1.2. Population 1 has rather normal marginal distributions. In population 2, one variable has a U-shaped distribution and the other a skewed distribution.

We have run many different populations of the kind illustrated in Tables 1.1 and 1.2, varying the number of categories, the cell probabilities, ρ, and the sample sizes. General conclusions that can be drawn from these Monte Carlo experiments are as follows:

☐ All correlations are biased downwards, but the bias for POLYCHOR (PM) is small and negligible for moderate sample sizes.

☐ POLYCHOR (PM), PMC-NS (KM–ordinal), and CANON (OM) do not appear to be sensitive to the shape of the marginal distributions.

☐ POLYCHOR (PM) is generally the best estimator, but the relative performances of PMC-NS (KM–ordinal) and CANON (OM) are improved as the number of categories increases, especially in moderate samples.

☐ POLYCHOR (PM) is almost always the best correlation in each sample in the sense of being closest to the true ρ. CANON (OM) is mostly second, and PMC-NS (KM–ordinal) is third. KENDALL is always the worst correlation, and SPEARMAN is only marginally better than PMC-RS.

☐ Only POLYCHOR (PM) appears to be a consistent estimator of ρ. Although variances of all the other correlations are small, their biases do not become small when the sample size increases.

1.9   An experiment with variables of different scale types

Four hundred observations were generated from a multivariate normal distribution with mean vector zero and covariance matrix

$$
\Sigma = \begin{bmatrix}
1.000 & & & & & \\
0.720 & 1.000 & & & & \\
0.378 & 0.336 & 1.000 & & & \\
0.324 & 0.288 & 0.420 & 1.000 & & \\
0.270 & 0.240 & 0.350 & 0.300 & 1.000 & \\
0.270 & 0.240 & 0.126 & 0.108 & 0.090 & 1.000
\end{bmatrix}
$$

This covariance matrix has been constructed to satisfy, exactly, a factor analysis model with two correlated factors and a clear simple structure

Table 1.1
Monte Carlo results on six correlation measures for ordinal variables

Population 1

$$\rho = 0.6$$

Thresholds for x : $-0.842,\quad 0.524$
Thresholds for y : $-0.852,\quad 0.524,\quad 1.282$

Probabilities

		y			
x	1	2	3	4	
1	0.100	0.090	0.009	0.001	0.200
2	0.090	0.293	0.092	0.025	0.500
3	0.010	0.117	0.099	0.074	0.300
	0.200	0.500	0.200	0.100	1.000

Results

		PMC-RS	SPEARMAN	KENDALL	CANON	PMC-NS	POLYCHOR
$N = 100$	Nbest	0	8	9	70	11	202
	Mean	0.4843	0.4869	0.3592	0.5122	0.4883	0.5867
	Variance	0.0053	0.0057	0.0078	0.0054	0.0055	0.0073
	Bias	−0.1157	−0.1131	−0.2408	−0.0878	−0.1117	−0.0133
	MSE	0.0187	0.0185	0.0658	0.0131	0.0180	0.0075
$N = 400$	Nbest	0	0	0	43	0	257
	Mean	0.4971	0.5008	0.3566	0.5091	0.5012	0.6001
	Variance	0.0014	0.0015	0.0019	0.0015	0.0015	0.0019
	Bias	−0.1029	−0.0992	−0.2434	−0.0909	−0.0988	−0.0001
	MSE	0.0120	0.0114	0.0612	0.0098	0.0112	0.0019
$N = 1000$	Nbest	0	0	0	3	0	297
	Mean	0.4985	0.5021	0.3606	0.5062	0.5030	0.6017
	Variance	0.0005	0.0005	0.0007	0.0005	0.0005	0.0007
	Bias	−0.1015	−0.0979	−0.2394	−0.0938	−0.0970	−0.0017
	MSE	0.0108	0.0101	0.0580	0.0093	0.0099	0.0007

Table 1.2
Monte Carlo results on six correlation measures for ordinal variables

Population 2

$\rho = 0.6$

Thresholds for x : $-0.604,\ -0.111,\ 0.111,\ 0.604$

Thresholds for y : $-1.645,\ -1.036,\ -0.674,\ -0.253,\ 0.126,\ 0.674$

Probabilities

x \ y	1	2	3	4	5	6	7	
1	0.039	0.059	0.045	0.051	0.036	0.030	0.013	0.273
2	0.007	0.021	0.024	0.036	0.034	0.037	0.025	0.183
3	0.002	0.007	0.009	0.015	0.016	0.021	0.018	0.088
4	0.002	0.009	0.014	0.017	0.032	0.048	0.052	0.183
5	0.001	0.004	0.008	0.021	0.032	0.065	0.143	0.273
	0.050	0.100	0.100	0.150	0.150	0.200	0.250	1.000

Results

		PMC-RS	SPEARMAN	KENDALL	CANON	PMC-NS	POLYCHOR
$N = 100$	Nbest	0	11	0	85	12	192
	Mean	0.5298	0.5381	0.0363	0.5696	0.5393	0.5972
	Variance	0.0024	0.0024	0.0020	0.0023	0.0023	0.0027
	Bias	−0.0702	−0.0619	−0.5637	−0.0304	−0.0607	−0.0028
	MSE	0.0073	0.0063	0.3197	0.0032	0.0060	0.0027
$N = 400$	Nbest	0	0	0	63	6	223
	Mean	0.5297	0.5386	0.0382	0.5551	0.5395	0.5969
	Variance	0.0015	0.0016	0.0011	0.0015	0.0015	0.0018
	Bias	−0.0703	−0.0614	−0.5618	−0.0449	−0.0605	−0.0031
	MSE	0.0064	0.0054	0.3167	0.0035	0.0052	0.0018
$N = 1000$	Nbest	0	0	0	40	0	260
	Mean	0.5331	0.5410	0.0431	0.5490	0.5415	0.5989
	Variance	0.0006	0.0006	0.0005	0.0005	0.0005	0.0006
	Bias	−0.0669	−0.0590	−0.5569	−0.0510	−0.0585	−0.0011
	MSE	0.0051	0.0041	0.3107	0.0031	0.0040	0.0006

(see Jöreskog, 1979). The following values were assigned to the thresholds $\alpha_1, \alpha_2, \ldots, \alpha_{k-1}$ of variables 2, 3, 4, and 6, where k is the number of categories.

Variable 2	Variable 3	Variable 4	Variable 6
(k = 7)	(k = 5)	(k = 3)	(k = 2)
$\alpha_1 = -1.64$	$\alpha_1 = -0.60$	$\alpha_1 = -0.67$	$\alpha_1 = -0.25$
$\alpha_2 = -1.04$	$\alpha_2 = -0.11$	$\alpha_2 = -0.67$	
$\alpha_3 = -0.67$	$\alpha_3 = -0.11$		
$\alpha_4 = -0.25$	$\alpha_4 = -0.60$		
$\alpha_5 = -0.13$			
$\alpha_6 = -0.67$			

These thresholds correspond to the following marginal probabilities.

Variable 2	Variable 3	Variable 4	Variable 6
$\pi_1 = 0.05$	$\pi_1 = 0.273$	$\pi_1 = 0.25$	$\pi_1 = 0.4$
$\pi_2 = 0.10$	$\pi_2 = 0.183$	$\pi_2 = 0.50$	$\pi_2 = 0.6$
$\pi_3 = 0.10$	$\pi_3 = 0.088$	$\pi_3 = 0.25$	
$\pi_4 = 0.15$	$\pi_4 = 0.183$		
$\pi_5 = 0.15$	$\pi_5 = 0.273$		
$\pi_6 = 0.20$			
$\pi_7 = 0.25$			

Thus, variable 2 is skewed, variable 3 has a U-shaped distribution, variable 4 is symmetrical, and variable 6 is dichotomous.

These four variables were then transformed to ordinal variables as follows:

If $x \leq \alpha_1$,   the value 1 was assigned to the observation x.

If $\alpha_{i-1} < x \leq \alpha_i$,   the value i was assigned to the observation x. $(i = 2, 3, \ldots, k - 1)$

If $\alpha_{k-1} < x$,   the value k was assigned to the observation x.

Variables 1 and 5 were unchanged. Finally, 20 percent of all entries in the data matrix were randomly changed to -9, representing missing observations. The first 20 cases of the data matrix generated in this way are as follows.

−2.14	2	1	−9	−0.60	1
−0.42	7	−9	−9	−0.55	2
−9.00	7	1	3	1.33	2
0.57	6	1	1	−1.96	2
−1.72	−9	5	−9	−0.88	2
−9.00	6	5	−9	−9.00	2
−0.42	4	2	1	−9.00	2
−9.00	5	4	2	−1.68	−9
0.57	7	1	2	−0.86	2
0.51	6	4	2	0.88	2
0.85	7	5	−9	−9.00	2
1.90	7	−9	2	1.54	1
−1.13	−9	5	2	2.45	−9
−0.03	2	−9	2	−0.75	−9
−2.20	−9	−9	1	−2.26	1
0.66	−9	2	1	1.06	2
−0.81	6	4	3	−0.28	2
−1.58	−9	1	−9	−0.56	−9
−0.56	−9	1	−9	−2.08	−9
0.95	6	−9	−9	−0.03	1

PRELIS was used to compute four types of correlation matrices using both pairwise and listwise deletion. This yielded eight estimated correlation matrices. Each is compared to the true correlation matrix Σ given above.

Results are shown in Table 1.3. (In Tables 1.3 and 1.4, columns for the four types of correlation matrices are labeled PMC-RS, PMC-NS, PMC-OS, and PP-PS, corresponding to the PRELIS options KM (continuous), KM (ordinal), OM, and PM, as defined on page 7.

Each of the eight correlation matrices was further analyzed with LISREL to fit a restricted (confirmatory) factor analysis model with two correlated factors. The factor loading matrix had three fixed zeroes in each column (see Jöreskog, 1979). The maximum likelihood (ML) method was used in LISREL to fit the model, even though there was no theoretical justification for using ML in this case. The sample size was assumed to be 280 for the four correlation matrices computed under pairwise deletion and 102 for the four correlation matrices computed under listwise deletion. Sample size affects only the chi-square values.

Results are shown in Table 1.4.

Comments on Tables 1.3 and 1.4

❑ In terms of bias and mean square error, there seems to be a clear
trend in the tables: PMC-RS and PMC-NS are most biased and have
the largest mean square error; PMC-OS performs somewhat better;
and PP-PS is least biased and has the smallest mean square error.
This holds for both pairwise and listwise deletion.

❑ In this case, pairwise deletion gave better results than listwise deletion. This is undoubtedly because 20 % of the observations were
missing at random, reducing the *effective sample size* under listwise
deletion to only 102, while the pairwise sample sizes varied from 240
to 328.

❑ The correlations in Table 1.3 were mostly underestimated. As can
be seen in Table 1.4, this results in underestimates of factor loadings
and in overestimates of unique variances.

❑ All eight correlation matrices generated by PRELIS were positive-
definite. As seen in Table 1.4, the ML method gave good results even
when some of the variables are ordinal. This demonstrates that, although normal-theory chi-square values and standard errors are not
valid, the ML method may still be used to fit the model to the data.

❑ Table 1.4 also reports three measures of overall fit: chi-square with
eight degrees of freedom, adjusted goodness of fit index (AGFI), and
root mean residual (RMSR). In this case, chi-square values and other
measures of fit behave quite normally.

❑ The numbers presented in Tables 1.3 and 1.4 represent a single
case study from which very well-established conclusions cannot be
drawn. To obtain clearer and more exact results, a full scale Monte
Carlo study should be undertaken.[5]

---

[5]See also page 189.

Table 1.3   Eight different correlation estimates

Simulated data, N = 400

Except for the first column, all numbers are deviations from the true value.
All numbers have been multiplied by 1000 and rounded.

True Value	Pairwise deletion				Listwise deletion			
	PMC-RS	PMC-NS	PMC-OS	PP-PS	PMC-RS	PMC-NS	PMC-OS	PP-PS
720	−16	−12	23	14	−22	−22	12	−2
378	−59	−57	−33	−34	−69	−59	−34	−42
336	−59	−44	−20	−7	−87	−88	−14	−54
324	−43	−43	−11	−17	−41	−41	−9	−18
288	−29	−17	12	25	−19	−9	94	32
420	−83	−81	−56	−16	8	−1	29	77
270	−34	−34	−34	−34	−51	−51	−51	−51
240	4	13	24	17	−32	−35	−25	−38
350	−49	−44	−20	−29	57	59	92	70
300	−14	−14	19	17	−59	−59	−31	−37
270	−98	−98	−51	−53	−118	−118	−77	−78
240	−17	−31	1	36	−48	−65	−14	−10
126	51	40	63	0	35	35	87	94
108	−125	−125	−76	−84	−159	−159	−49	−37
90	−53	−53	−43	−44	−119	−119	−153	−68
BIAS	−42	−40	−13	−14	−48	−49	−10	−11
MSE	59	57	38	35	74	74	65	54

Table 1.4   Eight different parameter estimates

Simulated data, N = 400

Except for the first column, all numbers are deviations from the true value.
All numbers have been multiplied by 1000 and rounded.

True Value	Pairwise deletion				Listwise deletion			
	PMC-RS	PMC-NS	PMC-OS	PP-PS	PMC-RS	PMC-NS	PMC-OS	PP-PS
900	−105	−59	−37	−11	−132	−18	−62	−10
800	33	43	61	6	4	−9	73	33
700	−89	−85	−66	−45	65	62	70	3
600	−44	−45	−10	20	−41	−50	−4	20
500	−1	1	18	−2	9	13	28	−2
300	−66	−74	−33	−11	−100	−110	−50	−46
600	−21	−12	−6	−17	−117	−110	−57	−102
190	178	103	66	22	221	32	108	−30
360	−54	−71	−101	−9	−6	14	−123	−54
510	117	111	88	61	−95	−91	−103	−4
640	51	52	12	−24	48	57	5	−24
750	1	−1	−18	2	−9	−13	−28	2
910	35	39	19	7	50	54	28	25
BIAS	3	0	−1	0	−8	−13	−9	−15
MSE	78	63	51	25	92	60	68	38
CHI-SQR	10.94	8.81	8.21	5.22	7.99	7.82	11.02	6.81
AGFI	0.967	0.973	0.975	0.984	0.939	0.940	0.914	0.946
RMSR	0.031	0.029	0.027	0.022	0.041	0.041	0.049	0.036

1.10   Six types of moment matrices

Some of the various types of moment matrices that the program can compute are defined in this section and illustrated by means of a small data set.

The basis of analysis in PRELIS is a *data matrix* $\mathbf{Z}$ with N rows and k columns:

$$\mathbf{Z} = \begin{bmatrix} z_{11} & z_{12} & \cdots & z_{1k} \\ z_{21} & z_{22} & \cdots & z_{2k} \\ \vdots & \vdots & \ddots & \vdots \\ z_{N1} & z_{N2} & \cdots & z_{Nk} \end{bmatrix}$$

The columns represent *variables*. The rows represent statistical units (individuals, companies, regions, occasions, etc.) on which the variables have been observed or measured.

In this manual we shall refer to a row of the data matrix as a *case* on which the variables have been observed or measured. A case may be a *single observation* (as when the row characterizes an individual) or a *multiple case* (as when the row characterizes a whole group of individuals with identical responses to the variables). When a row of the data matrix represents a pattern of observations, the row carries a *weight* equal to the number of individuals having the same responses.

Each element $z_{\alpha i}$ is a numeric value. For continuous variables, these values represent observations or measurements on an interval scale or ratio scale. For ordinal variables, the values represent arbitrary score values, such as 1, 2, 3, 4, and 5 of a 5-category Likert scale. Still other values in the data matrix may represent missing observations.

An example of such a data matrix is shown on the next page. It consists of 15 cases on four variables. (The sample size 25 is far too small to be useful in any LISREL model. Nevertheless, this small data set will be used here for illustrative purposes, as it is possible to check most of the computations by hand.)

Variables 1 and 2 are assumed to be ordinal variables. The three entries of "−9" are specified by the user to represent missing observations. PRELIS can handle missing data using pairwise or listwise deletion or by imputation. Pairwise and listwise deletion are discussed here. Imputation is discussed in *Imputation of missing values* on page 153 in Appendix B.

Case	Var 1	Var 2	Var 3	Var 4
1	1	3	−0.7	−0.4
2	2	4	2.3	1.6
3	3	3	1.2	1.7
4	1	−9	−0.4	−0.3
5	3	2	−1.2	−0.7
6	2	1	−9.0	1.2
7	2	1	0.8	0.3
8	3	3	1.6	1.5
9	1	2	−0.9	−9.0
10	1	4	−0.8	−0.8
11	1	1	0.7	0.8
12	1	2	1.1	1.3
13	1	1	−9.0	0.8
14	2	2	0.7	0.3
15	3	3	1.8	1.7
16	1	2	−0.9	−9.0
17	2	4	−0.8	−0.7
18	2	1	1.1	1.2
19	3	1	1.2	1.7
20	2	2	1.6	1.8
21	2	4	2.3	1.6
22	3	3	1.2	1.7
23	3	2	−1.2	−0.7
24	2	1	−9.0	1.2
25	2	1	0.8	0.3

Pairwise deletion

To begin with, we shall pretend that all four variables are continuous. Let n_{ij} be the number of cases having real observations on both variables i and j (the effective sample sizes under pairwise deletion). The n_{ij} form a symmetric matrix $\mathbf{N}$ of order $k \times k$. For the data of our small illustrative example the matrix $\mathbf{N}$ is:

$$\mathbf{N} = \begin{bmatrix} 25 & & & \\ 24 & 24 & & \\ 22 & 21 & 22 & \\ 23 & 22 & 20 & 23 \end{bmatrix}$$

Some of the moment matrices can now be defined.

The moment matrix (MM) is defined as the symmetric matrix $\mathbf{M} = (m_{ij})$ with elements

$$m_{ij} = (1/n_{ij}) \sum_\alpha z_{\alpha i} z_{\alpha j}$$

where the summation is over all cases with real observations on both variables i and j. This definition applies when $i = j$ as well. The elements of $\mathbf{M}$ represent moments about zero or mean squares and products. For the small data set:

$$\mathbf{M} = \begin{bmatrix} 4.440 & & & \\ 4.412 & 6.042 & & \\ 1.320 & 1.251 & 1.562 & \\ 1.664 & 1.562 & 1.246 & 1.395 \end{bmatrix}$$

The covariance matrix (CM) is defined as the symmetric matrix $\mathbf{S} = (s_{ij})$ with elements

$$s_{ij} = [1/(n_{ij} - 1)] \sum_\alpha (z_{\alpha i} - \bar{z}_i)(z_{\alpha j} - \bar{z}_j)$$

where

$$\bar{z}_i = (1/n_{ii}) \sum_\alpha z_{\alpha i} \quad \text{and} \quad \bar{z}_j = (1/n_{jj}) \sum_\alpha z_{\alpha j} \; .$$

Note that the means use all univariate nonmissing data whereas the covariances are based on all cases with nonmissing observations on both variables i and j. For our small data matrix:

$$\mathbf{S} = \begin{bmatrix} 0.623 & & & \\ 0.097 & 1.216 & & \\ 0.310 & 0.101 & 1.350 & \\ 0.216 & -0.083 & 0.896 & 0.881 \end{bmatrix}$$

Here, for example, $s_{21} = 0.097$ is based on 24 cases, $s_{11} = 0.623$ is based on 25 cases, and $s_{22} = 1.216$ is based on 24 cases.

The correlation matrix (KM) is the matrix $\mathbf{R} = (r_{ij})$ with elements

$$r_{ij} = s_{ij}/d_i d_j$$

where

$$d_i^2 = [1/(n_{ii} - 1)] \sum_\alpha (z_{\alpha i} - \bar{z}_i)^2$$

and

$$d_j^2 = [1/(n_{jj} - 1)] \sum_\alpha (z_{\alpha j} - \bar{z}_j)^2 \, .$$

In the standard deviations d_i and d_j, the sums are over all real observations on each variables i and j, respectively. With these definitions it can technically happen that $r_{ij}^2 > 1$, although this is unlikely in large samples. For the small data set:

$$\mathbf{R} = \begin{bmatrix} 1.000 & & & \\ 0.100 & 1.000 & & \\ 0.337 & 0.079 & 1.000 & \\ 0.292 & -0.081 & 0.822 & 1.000 \end{bmatrix}$$

The three matrices $\mathbf{M}$, $\mathbf{S}$, and $\mathbf{R}$ were computed without distinguishing between ordinal and continuous variables. Data values on ordinal variables were treated as if they came from interval scales. However, by declaring the first two variables to be ordinal, other types of correlation matrices can be obtained.

When some of the variables are declared ordinal, the arbitrary score values of these variables can be replaced with their corresponding normal scores before $\mathbf{M}$, $\mathbf{S}$, or $\mathbf{R}$ is computed.

For variable 2 in our small data set, the computation of the normal scores is as follows:

Category	Marginal Frequency	Upper Threshold	Normal Score
1	8	-0.431	-1.118
2	7	0.319	-0.103
3	5	0.967	0.532
4	4	$+\infty$	1.750

The resulting moment matrices are:

$$\mathbf{M} = \begin{bmatrix} 0.805 & & & \\ 0.051 & 0.989 & & \\ 0.345 & 0.052 & 1.562 & \\ 0.240 & -0.107 & 1.246 & 1.395 \end{bmatrix}$$

$$\mathbf{S} = \begin{bmatrix} 0.839 & & & \\ 0.054 & 1.032 & & \\ 0.361 & 0.055 & 1.350 & \\ 0.251 & -0.112 & 0.896 & 0.881 \end{bmatrix}$$

$$\mathbf{R} = \begin{bmatrix} 1.000 & & & \\ 0.058 & 1.000 & & \\ 0.339 & 0.046 & 1.000 & \\ 0.292 & -0.118 & 0.922 & 1.000 \end{bmatrix}$$

Besides the correlation matrix KM described above, there are four other types of correlation matrices, OM, PM, RM and TM, which can be used when some or all of the variables are ordinal. These correlation matrices consist of three different types of correlations. For each pair of variables one of the following three alternatives will occur:

1. When **both variables are continuous** (interval scaled), the product-moment correlation is computed from all complete pairs of observations. This correlation is the same in OM, PM, RM, and TM.

2. When **both variables are ordinal**, a contingency table is obtained from which the correlation is computed. Under OM, this correlation is the product-moment correlation of optimal scores or the canonical correlation (see Kendall & Stuart,1961, pp. 568–573). Under PM, this correlation is the maximum-likelihood estimate of the *polychoric correlation*, where an underlying bivariate normal distribution is assumed. Under RM, this is Spearman's rank correlation and under TM, this is Kendall's tau-c correlation.

3. When **one variable is ordinal and the other is continuous**, the program obtains the mean and variance of the continuous variable for each category of the ordinal variable and uses these summary statistics to compute the *polyserial correlation* (assuming again an

underlying bivariate normal distribution). Under OM, RM, and TM, a simple consistent estimator will be used, but under PM, a maximum-likelihood estimator will be used (see Jöreskog, 1986).

The end product of this procedure is a correlation matrix for all the variables, where each correlation has been estimated separately. Although it is rare in practice, experience indicates that such a correlation matrix sometimes fails to be positive-definite. When a correlation matrix that is not positive-definite is to be used to estimate a LISREL model, the ML or GLS method cannot be used. The ULS, WLS, or DWLS method must be used instead. Furthermore, even if the matrix of correlations is positive-definite, these correlations are unlikely to behave like ordinary sample moments, not even asymptotically. So, if one uses the ML or GLS methods for fitting the model, one should not rely on the normal theory standard errors and chi-square goodness-of-fit measures supplied by LISREL. Correct large sample standard errors and chi-square values can be obtained with WLS in LISREL.

When both variables are ordinal, information provided in the data may be represented as a contingency table. For the illustrative data, the contingency table for variables 1 and 2 is:

| | VAR 2 | | | | |
VAR 1	1	2	3	4	Marginal
1	2	3	1	1	7
2	5	2	0	3	10
3	1	2	4	0	7
Marginal	8	7	5	4	24

Let x and y be two ordinal variables with p and q categories, respectively. Let n_{ij} ($i = 1, 2, \ldots, p$, $j = 1, 2, \ldots, q$) be the corresponding frequencies in the contingency table.

Optimal scores for x and y are defined as two sets of ordered score values that maximize the product-moment correlations, subject to the constraints that the means are 0 and the variances are 1 (see Kendall & Stuart, 1961, pp. 568–573). The product-moment correlation of these optimal scores, sometimes called *canonical correlation*, is obtained as the second largest eigenvalue of a symmetric matrix formed from the elements of the contingency table.

The *polychoric correlation* is not a correlation between a pair of score values. Rather it is an estimate of the correlation between two latent variables η and ξ underlying y and x, where η and ξ are assumed to have a bivariate normal distribution. For our illustrative data, the polychoric correlation between variables 1 and 2 is estimated as 0.098.

This latent correlation can be estimated by the maximum-likelihood method based on the multinomial distribution of the cell frequencies in the contingency table. The estimation procedure follows Olsson (1979), but the computational algorithm has been considerably improved since LISREL 6. The algorithm in PRELIS is often 20 times faster than that of LISREL 6.

Next, consider the third case, when one variable is ordinal and one variable is continuous. In our small data set, there will be four such pairs of variables: (3,1), (3,2), (4,1), and (4,2). In the illustration below, we use the pair (3,1). Let x be an ordinal variable with p categories, and let y be a continuous variable. As before, let n_i be the number of cases in category i of x. Corresponding to these cases, there will be n_i values on y denoted:

$$y_{i1}, \; y_{i2}, \; \ldots, \; y_{in_i}$$

Let $\bar{y}_i$ and s_i^2 be the mean and unbiased variance of these values. (If $n_i = 1$, the variance is zero and this category cannot be used in the computations. However, the required correlation can still be computed, provided there are at least two categories with $n_i > 1$.) For the pair (3,1), these summary statistics are:

Category	Number of Observations	Mean	Standard Deviation
1	7	−0.271	0.826
2	8	1.100	1.006
3	7	0.657	1.290

The *polyserial correlation* is the correlation between the observed variable y and a latent variable ξ, where y and ξ are assumed to have a bivariate normal distribution. This can be estimated by the maximum-likelihood method as described by Jöreskog (1986). Under OM, Jöreskog's Method 1 is used; under PM, Jöreskog's Method 5 is used.

For our illustrative data, the correlation matrices obtained under the options OM and PM are:

$$\mathbf{O} = \begin{bmatrix} 1.000 & & & \\ 0.197 & 1.000 & & \\ 0.424 & 0.060 & 1.000 & \\ 0.313 & -0.111 & 0.822 & 1.000 \end{bmatrix}$$

$$\mathbf{P} = \begin{bmatrix} 1.000 & & & \\ 0.098 & 1.000 & & \\ 0.362 & 0.051 & 1.000 & \\ 0.340 & -0.112 & 0.822 & 1.000 \end{bmatrix}$$

Listwise deletion

So far, we have dealt with pairwise deletion. With *listwise deletion*, all cases with missing observations are deleted first so that the data matrix reduces effectively to a matrix without missing observations. All the definitions above still apply. The main difference is that under listwise deletion, all computations are based on the same cases. This will guarantee that all the matrices obtained under MM, CM, and KM are non-negative-definite. Correlation matrices obtained under OM and PM still cannot be guaranteed to be non-negative-definite, as they may consist of different types of correlations.

1.11 Producing weight matrices and fit functions

As one of its options, PRELIS produces the *asymptotic covariance matrix* of estimated covariances and correlations. This section explains what this matrix is and how it can be used to produce *weight matrices* for certain fit functions in LISREL. A fuller and more technical account of these topics is given in Appendix A in Jöreskog, *et al.* (1999).

A general family of fit functions for analysis-of-covariance structures may be written (see, for example, Browne, 1984)

$$
\begin{aligned}
F(\boldsymbol{\theta}) &= (\mathbf{s} - \boldsymbol{\sigma})'\mathbf{W}^{-1}(\mathbf{s} - \boldsymbol{\sigma}) \\
&= \sum_{g=1}^{k} \sum_{h=1}^{g} \sum_{i=1}^{k} \sum_{j=1}^{i} w^{gh,ij}(s_{gh} - \sigma_{gh})(s_{ij} - \sigma_{ij})
\end{aligned} \qquad (1.1)
$$

where

$$
\mathbf{s}' = (s_{11}, s_{21}, s_{22}, s_{31}, \ldots, s_{kk})
$$

is a vector of the elements in the lower half, including the diagonal, of the covariance matrix $\mathbf{S}$ of order $k \times k$ used to fit the model to the data;

$$
\boldsymbol{\sigma}' = (\sigma_{11}, \sigma_{21}, \sigma_{22}, \sigma_{31}, \ldots, \sigma_{kk})
$$

is the vector of corresponding elements of $\Sigma(\boldsymbol{\theta})$ reproduced from the model parameters $\boldsymbol{\theta}$; and $w^{gh,ij}$ is a typical element of a positive-definite matrix $\mathbf{W}^{-1}$ of order $p \times p$, where $p = k(k + 1)/2$. In most cases, the elements of $\mathbf{W}^{-1}$ are obtained by inverting a matrix $\mathbf{W}$ whose typical element is denoted $w_{gh,ij}$. The usual way of choosing $\mathbf{W}$ in weighted least squares is to let $w_{gh,ij}$ be a consistent estimate of the asymptotic covariance between s_{gh} and s_{ij} but, in principle, any positive-definite matrix $\mathbf{W}$ may be used. To estimate the model parameters $\boldsymbol{\theta}$, the fit function is minimized with respect to $\boldsymbol{\theta}$.

Under very general assumptions, if the model holds in the population and if the sample variances and covariances in $\mathbf{S}$ converge in probability to the corresponding elements in the population covariance matrix Σ as the sample size increases, any such fit function will give a consistent estimator of $\boldsymbol{\theta}$. In practice, numerical results obtained by one fit function are often close enough to the results that would be obtained by another fit function, to allow the same substantive interpretation.

Further assumptions must be made, however, if one needs an asymptotically correct chi-square test of goodness of fit and asymptotically correct standard errors of parameter estimates.

"Classical" theory for covariance structures (see, for example, Browne, 1974 or Jöreskog, 1981) assumes that the asymptotic variances and covariances of the elements of $\mathbf{S}$ are of the form

$$\text{ACov}(s_{gh}, s_{ij}) = (1/N)(\sigma_{gi}\sigma_{hj} + \sigma_{gj}\sigma_{hi}) \qquad (1.2)$$

where N is the total sample size. This holds, in particular, if the observed variables have a multivariate normal distribution, or if $\mathbf{S}$ has a Wishart distribution. The GLS (generalized least squares) and ML (maximum-likelihood) methods available in LISREL and their chi-square values and standard errors are based on these assumptions. The GLS method corresponds to using a matrix $\mathbf{W}$ in (1.1) whose general element is

$$w_{gh,ij} = (1/N)(s_{gi}s_{hj} + s_{gj}s_{hi}) \qquad (1.3)$$

The fit function for ML is not of the form (1.1) but may be shown to be equivalent to using a $\mathbf{W}$ of the form (1.3), with s replaced with an estimate of σ that is updated in each iteration.

In recent fundamental work by Browne (1982, 1984), this classical theory for covariance structures has been generalized to any multivariate distribution for continuous variables satisfying very mild assumptions. This approach uses a $\mathbf{W}$ matrix with typical element

$$w_{gh,ij} = m_{ghij} - s_{gh}s_{ij} \qquad (1.4)$$

where

$$m_{ghij} = (1/N) \sum_{\alpha=1}^{N} (z_{\alpha g} - \bar{z}_g)(z_{\alpha h} - \bar{z}_h)(z_{\alpha i} - \bar{z}_i)(z_{\alpha j} - \bar{z}_j)$$

are the fourth-order central moments. Using such a $\mathbf{W}$ in (1.1) gives what Browne calls "asymptotically distribution free best GLS estimators" for which correct asymptotic chi-squares and standard errors may be obtained. As shown by Browne, this $\mathbf{W}$ matrix also may be used to compute correct asymptotic chi-squares and standard errors for estimates that have been obtained by the classical ML and GLS methods. When $\mathbf{W}$ is defined by (1.4), we call the fit function WLS (weighted least squares) to distinguish it from GLS where $\mathbf{W}$ is defined by (1.3). WLS and GLS are different forms of weighted least squares: WLS is asymptotically distribution free, while GLS is based on normal theory.

While WLS is attractive in theory, it presents several difficulties in practical applications. First, the matrix $\mathbf{W}$ is of order $p \times p$ and has $p(p+1)/2$ distinct elements. This increases rapidly with k, demanding large amounts of computer memory when k is at all large. For example, when $k = 20$, $\mathbf{W}$ has 22155 distinct elements. Second, to estimate moments of fourth order with reasonable precision requires very large samples. Third, when there are missing observations in the data, different moments involved in (1.4) may be based on different numbers of cases unless listwise deletion is used. When pairwise deletion is used, it is not clear how to deal with this problem.

Finally, Browne's (1984) development is a theory for sample covariance matrices for continuous variables. In practice, however, correlation matrices often are analyzed; that is, covariance matrices scaled by stochastic standard deviations. The elements of such a correlation matrix do not have asymptotic variances and covariances of the form (1.2), even if $\mathbf{S}$ has a Wishart distribution. In PRELIS, an estimate of the asymptotic covariance matrix of the estimated correlations can also be obtained under the same general assumptions of non-normality. This approach can be used when some or all of the variables are ordinal or censored, after the raw scores are replaced by normal scores. PRELIS can also compute estimates of the asymptotic variances and covariances of estimated polychoric and polyserial correlations. This approach is similar to that of Muthén (1984), but the PRELIS estimates are much simpler and faster to compute.

A correlation matrix estimated in PRELIS with the KM or PM option has $q = k(k-1)/2$ estimated correlations and, as a consequence, the asymptotic covariance matrix of these correlations is of order $q \times q$. To obtain the weight matrix to be used in LISREL, this covariance matrix must be inverted. The inversion is not performed by PRELIS but is part of LISREL. The asymptotic covariance matrix of estimated coefficients obtained by PRELIS may be saved in a file that can be read directly by LISREL.

To sum up: whenever possible in PRELIS, an estimate of the asymptotic covariance matrix of the elements of the estimated moment matrix is provided. Currently, such asymptotic covariance matrices are available for sample covariance, moment, and augmented moment matrices and matrices of product-moment (Pearson), polychoric, and/or polyserial correlations. Asymptotic covariance matrices are not yet available for OM, RM, and TM matrices.[6]

Computation of asymptotic covariance matrices of estimated coefficients is very time-consuming and demands large amounts of memory when the number of variables is large. An alternative approach, which may be used even when the number of variables is large, is to compute only the asymptotic variances of the estimated coefficients. Let w_{gh} be an estimate of the asymptotic variance of s_{gh}. These estimates may be used with a fit function of the form:

$$F(\boldsymbol{\theta}) = \sum_{g=1}^{k} \sum_{h=1}^{g} (1/w_{gh})(s_{gh} - \sigma_{gh})^2 \qquad (1.5)$$

This corresponds to using a diagonal weight matrix $\mathbf{W}^{-1}$ in (1.1). In LIS-REL this is called DWLS (diagonally weighted least squares). This does not lead to asymptotically efficient estimates of model parameters but is offered as a compromise between unweighted least squares (ULS) and fully weighted least squares (WLS). The DWLS method can also be used when correlation matrices (KM or PM) are analyzed.

---

[6]However, see page 169.

2 General instructions for the problem run

2.1 Single group analysis

Unlike LISREL, which can analyze data from several groups simultaneously, PRELIS can only analyze data from one group at a time, because it reads each data set twice: first, for univariate screening; then, to compute the requested correlations/covariances.

Raw data may be available from several groups. If each group is to be analyzed separately, the data must be read from separate files. If the groups will be jointly analyzed, all data must first be combined into one file (see the section *Merging files*, page 162 in Appendix B on how to do that with PRELIS). The following combinations of these two approaches may occasionally be useful.

Suppose all variables are continuous and suppose the groups differ in mean vectors but not in standard deviations. First run all groups as a single group and record the standard deviations. Then run each group separately and scale the variables by the inverse of the standard deviation. The resulting estimated covariance matrices for each group are then such that their weighted average is a correlation matrix.

Suppose all variables are ordinal. First run all groups as a single group and transform all variables to normal scores. Then run the normal scores for each group separately to estimate a covariance matrix for each group.

In both of these cases, the resulting covariance matrices can be used in a multisample analysis in LISREL. See also *Thresholds* on page 176 in Appendix B.

31

2.2 Files

Three files must be specified for each problem:

1. INPUT file, containing commands to be read by PRELIS. How PRELIS commands are written is explained in Chapter 3. This file is also called *command file*.
2. DATA file, where raw data is stored to be read by the program. This information is provided in the command file.
3. OUTPUT file, where printed output from PRELIS will be given. This file is written by the program.

In addition to these necessary files, other files may be specified in the input file, such as a file for labels that will be read by the program, files for storing various parts of the output from PRELIS to be used by LISREL, etc.

Ways of specifying files for PRELIS vary with computers and operating systems. Typically, files are specified directly in the input file by *filename(s)*; with some operating systems, input and output files are specified when the program is invoked.

2.3 Command names

Note: Throughout this manual, significant characters of PRELIS command names, options, keywords, and character values are printed in a SWISS typeface.

Just as in LISREL, PRELIS is controlled by a number of commands, each beginning with a command name. (Some PRELIS command names are the same as in LISREL, but their options and keywords may be different.) As in LISREL, each problem for PRELIS begins with a data description command (DA), optionally preceded with one or more title lines, and ends with an output command (OU).

Command names may contain any number of characters (no blanks), but only the first two characters are significant to the program.

The following command names are recognized by PRELIS.

All these commands are described in detail in Chapter 3.

♯	DA	Data parameters
⋆	LA	Labels
⋆	RA	Raw data
♯	OR	Ordinal variables
♯	CO	Continuous variables
♯	CA	Censored above variables
♯	CB	Censored below variables
♯	CE	Censored above and below variables
♯	FI	Fixed or x variables
♯	RE	Recode variables
♯	CL	Labels for categories of ordinal variables
♯	NE	New variable
♯	PO	Power transformation
♯	LO	Log transformation
♯	SC	Select cases
♯	SD	Select cases and delete variables
♯	IM	Imputation of missing values
♯	MI	Missing value specification
♯	WE	Weight variable
♯	HT	Homogeneity test
♯	ET	Equal thresholds
♯	FT	Fixed thresholds
♯	MT	Marginal thresholds
♯	RG	Regression
♯	OU	Output

♯	*requires options and/or keywords*
⋆	*may require special syntax*

2.4   Options and keywords

Note: Throughout this manual, significant characters of PRELIS command names, options, keywords, and character values are printed in a SWISS typeface.

When options or keywords are entered commands, these rules apply:

- Options or keywords may contain any number of characters (no blanks), but only the first two are significant to the program.
- Most keywords require a numeric value; some require a string (character value).
- A string may contain any number of characters as long as the first two are correct.
- Options are switches: only the presence or absence of the option is significant.
- The order of options and keywords on each command is arbitrary.
- Options and/or keywords are separated by one or more blanks.
- Spaces before and after equal signs are optional.

Example

In the following examples of PRELIS commands, DA is the command name and NI and TR are the keywords. The keyword values assigned are 17, a numeric integer value, for NI and PA, a character value, for TR.

These commands are all *correct*:

```
DA NI=17 TR=PA
DATA NINPUT = 17 TREATMENT = PAIRWISE
DAtaparameters NInputvariables = 17 TR = PA
DAta TREAT = PAirwise NInputvar = 17
DA NI= 17 TR =PA
```

These are *incorrect* examples:

```
DATA PARAMETERS NI = 17 TR = PA
DA Number-of-inputvariables=17 TR=PA
```

The first line has an incorrect option (PA), while the second line contains a nonexistent keyword NU.

2.5 Physical lines

It is possible to string several PRELIS commands together on one physical
line by separating them with semicolons. Each physical line may contain
up to 127 characters. For example, these two physical lines

```
DA NI=9 NO=427 MI=-99; LA FI=LABELS
MI -9 MOEDUC; OR MOEDUC - FAEDUC
```

contain four commands. If these physical lines have a return character at
the end, semicolons after LABELS or FAEDUC are optional.

2.6 Order of commands

The order in which PRELIS commands are entered is arbitrary, with the
following exceptions:

1. The DA command must come first, optionally preceded with one or
   more title lines.
2. All commands (such as OR, CO, MI, PO, etc.) with labels in their
   varlists must come *after the labels have been read*. One cannot refer
   to a label unless the label has first been defined with an LA command.
3. The OU command must always be last.

Otherwise, commands can appear in any order. For example, labels may
be read before or after the raw data, and MI commands may come before
or after OR and CO commands.

It is important to remember, however, that the order in which commands
appear determines how the program will interpret information provided:
information given on one command can override information on all commands appearing before it. Note also that the order of the commands influences the order of the computations. See the next section and page 164
in Appendix B for details.

2.7   Order of computations

Regardless of the order in which commands are entered, PRELIS computations are done in the following order (see also page 164 in Appendix B):

1. All transformations requested on PO, LO, RE, and NE commands and all selection of cases and deletion of variables (with SC and SD commands) are done first. These operations have immediate effect and are done in the order that they appear in the command file.
2. Treatment of missing values. First imputation is done, if requested, then listwise deletion.
3. Classification of variables into fixed, ordinal, censored, and continuous.
4. Bootstrap sampling, if requested.
5. Computation of statistics.

2.8   Workspace

PRELIS uses dynamic memory allocation. After all commands for a problem have been read and interpreted, the program computes the number of bytes of memory it needs to run the problem completely.

If the program is properly installed in the computer, the program will also know how much memory is available to the program at runtime.

If the amount of memory available is insufficient to run a problem, the program prints FATAL ERROR 308 (see Appendix A). The error message will include the amount of memory needed and the amount of memory available. Processing of this particular problem will be discontinued. PRELIS will then proceed to the next problem, if any.

If memory is adequate and a problem runs to completion, the program prints out how much workspace was used and what percentage of available workspace this represents.

2.9   Restrictions

PRELIS has the following built-in restrictions:

- ☐ Polychoric and polyserial correlations will not be computed unless the pairwise sample size is at least 20.
- ☐ The number of categories in an ordinal variable can be no more than 15. If a variable has more than 15 distinct values, not counting missing values, it will be treated as continuous.
- ☐ For each problem, the number of RG commands in the input file can be no more than 10. All RG commands beyond the tenth will be ignored.

2.10   Stacked problems in one run

After the program has read an OU command, it will automatically read the next problem unless an end-of-file is encountered. Any number of problems may be stacked one after another and analyzed in one run. When several problems are stacked like this, outputs for each problem will be stacked one after another in the same order in the output file. Matrices saved with keywords on the OU command, like SM (save moment matrix), SA (save asymptotic covariance matrix), or SV (save asymptotic variances), may also be stacked by specifying the same filename in each problem.

The examples below illustrate stacked input and output as well as physical lines and PRELIS commands. Each pair of physical lines corresponds to one problem; except for the title, all the PRELIS commands for each problem are contained in one physical line. The example uses the small data matrix of order 12 by 4, described in the section *Six types of moment matrices* in Chapter 1, page 18.

The problems treat the first two variables as ordinal and compute the five correlation matrices MM, CM, KM, OM, and PM.

Note: the last problem will not run completely because of the sample size restriction described above. Output from these runs will be stacked in the same order.

```
TEST OF PRELIS RUN 1
DA NI=4 MI=-9 TR=PA;RA=TSTDATA RE;OR 1 2;CO 3 4;OU  MA=MM
TEST OF PRELIS RUN 2
DA NI=4 MI=-9 TR=PA;RA=TSTDATA RE;OR 1 2;CO 3 4;OU  MA=CM
TEST OF PRELIS RUN 3
DA NI=4 MI=-9 TR=PA;RA=TSTDATA RE;OR 1 2;CO 3 4;OU  MA=KM
TEST OF PRELIS RUN 4
DA NI=4 MI=-9 TR=PA;RA=TSTDATA RE;OR 1 2;CO 3 4;OU  MA=OM
TEST OF PRELIS RUN 5
DA NI=4 MI=-9 TR=PA;RA=TSTDATA RE;OR 1 2;CO 3 4;OU  MA=PM
```

2.11   How to use FORTRAN formats

The easiest and most convenient way to enter labels or raw data is to use free format, in which labels or data values of varying lengths are simply separated by one or more blanks. But you may prefer to include certain options on LA and RA commands so that FORTRAN formats may be utilized. (For exact instructions, see command descriptions in Chapter 3.)

There are three possible reasons for using FORTRAN formats instead of free format:

- ❑ You want to use a data file generated by another program that has no blanks or commas separating items.
- ❑ You are entering data in which all numeric values have the same number of decimal places; using a FORTRAN format will eliminate the need to enter decimal points.
- ❑ You want certain variables for each case to be eliminated, or skipped, in some of your program runs.

A FORTRAN format tells PRELIS how to read your data by specifying exactly where on every line each successive label or numeric value begins and ends. You might, for example, ask the program to read a line of labels entered as HEIGHTWEIGHTAGEIQ. Using the appropriate format designation (A6,A6,A3,A2), you can tell the program to interpret this line as the four labels HEIGHT, WEIGHT, AGE, and IQ.

Whether used for raw data or for labels, all FORTRAN formats require attention to two details:

☐ The data (labels or numeric data values) must be entered precisely as required for the format you specify. Failure to do so will lead to FATAL ERROR 407, which will stop the program. (See Appendix A.)

☐ Specification of a FORTRAN format must begin with a left parenthesis and end with a right parenthesis. Parentheses may also appear within the format, but for every left parenthesis there must be a right parenthesis. In other words, the total number of left parentheses must be the same as the total number of right parentheses. If this is not the case, FATAL ERROR 408 will occur and stop the program. (See Appendix A.)

NOTES

A carriage return or line feed ends each line of data. Therefore, neither of these is allowed *within* a line. (See Example 5, below.)

In general, a forward slash (/) in an F-format means *skip the rest of this line and continue on the next line.* (See Example 8, below.)

In Examples 1 and 2 below, we explain formats for *labels*, and in Examples 3 through 8, formats for *raw data*.

For labels, an A-format must be used.

Within each field, the label must be exactly as typed. Blanks (spaces) are counted as characters belonging either to a label or to its neighbor(s), depending on the column number.

Example 1: Labels

FORTRAN A-format (5A8) means there are 5 labels on each line, and each label (including blanks) occupies exactly 8 columns or characters (including blanks). Whatever appears within these 8 spaces will be read as the label.

first label	in columns 1–8
second label	in columns 9–16
third label	in columns 17–24
fourth label	in columns 25–32
fifth label	in columns 33–40

It might be represented visually as:

```
1-------2-------3-------4-------5-------
1111111122222222333333334444444455555555
```

Example 2: Labels

Another possible format specified as (A5,A8,A7,A3,A8) means there are only five labels per line, with no uniform length set for all of the labels:

first label	5 characters	in columns 1–5
second label	8 characters	in columns 6–13
third label	7 characters	in columns 14–20
fourth label	3 characters	in columns 21–23
fifth label	8 characters	in columns 24–31

It might be represented visually as:

```
1----2-------3------4--5-------
111112222222233333334444555555555
```

For raw data, an F-format must be used.

NOTE: NI, the number of input variables, is crucially important to the proper functioning of PRELIS. If this value is not entered on the DA command in the input file, FATAL ERROR 402 will stop the program.

Example 3: Raw data; NI = 10

Each case will have 10 data values (one value for each variable), all with decimals. Suppose that for one of the cases, these are the values:

```
38.60   13.63   16.96   24.62   8.00   27.22   5.60   4.81   6.27   5.16
```

The line above shows how these data could be entered in free format, with each value separated from its neighbor(s) by two blanks.

If you prefer not to type all those decimal points, you could specify the FORTRAN format (10F5.2), and enter the same data this way:

```
3860 1363 1696 2462   800 2722   560   481   627   516
```

The number '10' in the format designation above means there will be a total of 10 data values on each line. The number '5.2' means

(a) each data value will have a field of 5 positions, and

(b) the last 2 digits within each field of 5 will be decimals.

The program will insert a decimal point after the third position in each field (counting from the left).

Note: a carriage return or line feed ends each line of data; neither of these is allowed within a line.

Example 4: Raw data; NI = 55

Now suppose that instead of 10 variables you have 55 variables, but you like the F-format used in Example 3. The only change required is to specify the format as (55F5.2).

The same rules as in Example 3 will still pertain, except that this time each one of your lines is going to be 275 characters long (5 positions per value times 55 values). On your screen this one long line may appear as three lines of 80 characters plus one line of 35 characters.

Example 5: Raw data; NI = 55

If, as in Example 4, you are bothered by the discrepancy between the four lines you see on your screen and what the program interprets as only one long line, you could produce the same output by using the format (15F5.2/15F5.2/15F5.2/15F5.2/15F5.2). The only difference required in data entry would be to enter a carriage return or line feed in column 76 or later of each line of data. The program will read five lines for each case instead of only one, continuing to read until 55 variables have been located. The forward slash (/) signals that the next data entry should be read from the next line.

Example 6: Raw data; NI = 4

An F-format can be useful when your data values vary considerably in magnitude. The line

```
123.4567   0.44   9876543.8   4.76
```

could be entered very quickly as

```
123456704498765438476
```

if the format (F7.4,F3.2,F8.1,F3.2) has been specified.

Example 7: Raw data; NI = 3

Using the same line of data as in Example 6, suppose that NI = 3 (not 4) because you only want to include the variables 1, 2, and 4 in your analysis, skipping-over the third variable. This is easily achieved by specifying the format (F7.4,F3.2,8X,F3.2). Because the third variable has been replaced with 8X, the 8 columns after the first 10 columns will be skipped-over and the data will be read as

```
1234567044476
```

Step-by-step, this process may be represented visually as

```
1234567044987654387476    original data
1------2--3--------4--     breaks for 4 values in Example 6
1111111222xxxxxxxx444      columns for 3 values + 1 skipped value
1234567044xxxxxxxx476      data for 3 values + 1 skipped value
1234567044476             data read by program in Example 7
```

Example 8: Raw data; NI = 10

What if your data values extend over more than one line (as in Example 5, above), and you want to skip one or more variables (as in Example 7, above)?

Assume that you already ran the program once with the format (5F10.3 / 5F10.3), with 5 data values on the first line and 5 data values on the second line.

Your output indicated that variables 2, 3, 4, and 5 should be excluded from analysis on the next run. You can do this very simply by making a slight change in the format specification to (F10.3/5F10.3). This format means:

- ☐ read variable 1 on line 1
- ☐ skip all remaining variables on line 1
- ☐ go to line 2
- ☐ read 5 variables on line 2

A forward slash (/) in an —swr F-format means *skip the rest of this line and continue on the next line.*

Exercises based on data used in Example 8

Which of the 10 variables (5 on the first line, 5 on the second line) would be read by each of these formats?

```
(F10.3,10X,3F10.3/5F10.3)              Answer: 1,3,4,5,6,7,8,9,10
(2F10.3/20X,3F10.3)                    Answer: 1,2,8,9,10
(F10.3,10X,F10.3,10X,F10.3/20X,3F10.3) Answer: 1,3,5,8,9,10
(F10.3,10X,3F10.3/F10.3,10X,3F10.3)    Answer: 1,3,4,5,6,8,9,10
```

For more information about various kinds of FORTRAN formats, consult a FORTRAN textbook (usually available in mainframe computer centers).

2.12 Practical advice about data screening

If you have a large data file, it may be useful to screen it before proceeding with elaborate analysis. This simple input file can be used to determine the actual values present for each variable.

```
DA NI= number of input variables
LA
 labels
RA= filename where raw data is stored
OR ALL
OU
```

2.13 System Files

The current versions of PRELIS and LISREL generate several system files through which they can communicate with each other. These system files are binary files and can therefore be read very fast. Some of these system files can be used directly by users. Here we present the PRELIS system file, for all other system files see Jöreskog, *et al.* (1999).

The PRELIS System File

A PRELIS system file, or a PSF file for short is created when the user specifies RA=*filename*.PSF on the OU command.

Its use is recommended especially now that the analysis features in PRELIS have been expanded. Once the user finds the dataset in good shape, after taking care of missing values, outliers, recoding, etc., the creation of a PSF file makes further analysis of the data with PRELIS easier and faster.

For example, once the PRELIS system file has been created, say TEST.PSF, the example above may be abbreviated to:

```
SY=TEST.PSF
OR ALL
OU
```

The SY command replaces the DA, LA, and RA commands.

3 PRELIS commands

A PRELIS command file is created by the user for each problem run. This file is composed of commands that give specific instructions to PRELIS about where to find data, how to analyze data, where to save results, and how to print output.

This chapter explains in detail all the commands available in PRELIS, their proper specifications, the options and keywords each one utilizes, and it gives some very brief examples. In Chapter 4, Appendix B, and Appendix C, more extensive examples are discussed.[1]

A brief overview of the structure of a PRELIS command file is as follows.

1. Title line(s)   *Optional*
2. DA command (data specifications)   *Required*
3. LA command (labels)   *Optional*
4. RA command (raw data)   *Required*
5. One or more of the twenty-two other commands available
   to specify various attributes of each problem run   *Optional*
6. OU command (output)   *Required*

For each problem run, at least the three commands DA (data specification), RA (where and how to read the data), and OU (output specification) are required, in that order. Title lines, if any, should be entered before the DA commmand, the LA (variable labels) should be given before any other

---

[1] These extensive examples are all included on disk with the PRELIS program itself.

command refers to those labels, and the OU command should always be last.

All other commands may be entered, in no particular order, between the RA and the OU commands. Note however that the order of those commands influences the order of the computations. See page 164 in Appendix B for details.

Only two letters in the name of each command, option, or keyword need be entered. In the following descriptions of commands, these two letters are shown in a SWISS typeface.

PURPOSE

To give information to identify the problem.

FORMAT

... *text* ...
... *text* ...

NOTES

The first entry in each problem's command file may be one or more title lines. No two-letter symbol is required to identify it as the title; the fact that it comes first is sufficient. Any alphanumeric characters are acceptable for use in title lines, with one exception: do not start a title line with the characters 'DA' (in any combination of upper and lower case), because those two characters signal to the program the start of the DA command (see below) and, therefore, the end of the title line(s). To avoid this problem, it is good practice to start each title line with the comment character(s): ! or /*, indicating that everything on that line is a comment.

Title lines may be as short as one character, one word, or one line of 127 characters. But the program can read as many title lines as you care to enter.

The complete title will be printed at the beginning of your output. It can contain any information you want to include as a heading for the problem. Some examples:

- o describe the data
- o mark the position of a problem in a long sequence of problem runs
- o assign a catalog number to the paper printout before filing

PURPOSE
Specifies global characteristics of the raw data.

FORMAT

DA   NI=$k, l, m, \ldots$ NO= | **0** |
    number of cases   TR= | **LI** |
  PA

MI=*global missing value(s)*   RP= | **1** |
no. of repetitions

KEYWORDS

NI   Number of input variables
Default: None; required keyword.

The value of k must be specified or the program will stop. The number of variables is limited only by machine capacity.

When merging input files (see page 162 in Appendix B), a list of values should be entered. This list corresponds to the number of variables in the input files as specified with the RA command, in the same order.

NO   Number of cases
Default: NO=0

Equal to the sample size N (the number of statistical units or cases) on which the NI variables have been measured or observed. NO should also be equal to the number of rows in the data matrix. If sample size N is unknown, you may either omit NO or set NO $= 0$ and the program will compute N.

TR   Treatment of missing data
Default: TR=LI (listwise deletion)

LI designates listwise deletion. All cases with missing observations will be deleted. Computations will be based only on cases with real observations on all variables.

PA indicates pairwise deletion. For each pair of variables, computations will be based on all cases with real observations on both variables.

MI   Global value(s) for missing observations
Default: none (MI is optional)
One or more numeric values in the raw data can be assigned to represent missing observations in *all* variables.
Instead of a single value, a range of values may be used.

If, instead, missing values are *not* global but vary with variables, omit MI and use MI commands to list the specific missing value(s) for each variable or set of variables.

RP   Number of repetitions
Default: RP=1
This keyword is new with PRELIS 2. It is intended for Monte Carlo and bootstrap studies (see Appendix C).

For example, RP=100 means *repeat 100 times* and has the same effect as stacking 100 command files after each other, *i.e.*, the command file will be read and executed 100 times.

NOTES

See also the sections *Specification of missing values* (p. 152) and *Imputation of missing values* (p. 153) in Appendix B.

The keyword MC, specifying the maximum number of distinct, non-missing values (categories) for an ordinal variable, is not longer supported in PRELIS 2 (see also Appendix B, page 146).

PRELIS 2 will automatically classify all variables with less than 16 distinct, non-missing values as ordinal, the remaining variables as continuous. This default classification may be changed explicitly with OR, CO, CA, CB, or CE commands (see below).

Treatment of missing values is done after all data manipulations. If imputation is requested, this is done first. If TR is default or if TR=LI on the DA command, all cases with missing values remaining after imputation will be eliminated and all further computations will be based on the listwise sample. If TR=PA on the DA command, no deletion of cases will be made in the raw data.

Note that if TR=PA (pairwise deletion) on the DA command, not all of the statistics that are listed in the output with listwise deletion can be obtained. With pairwise deletion, all univariate statistics will be based on all cases present for each variable, and all bivariate statistics will be based on all cases present for each pair of variables. No multivariate statistics will be given.

PURPOSE

To assign names to variables.

FORMAT

LA   FI=*filename* FO

(Character variable format statement)

Data (variable labels)

KEYWORD

FI   User specified name of file containing the labels. Use this specification only if labels will be read from some external file, instead
of being typed into the PRELIS command file itself. With PRELIS 2
the shorter command format

    LA=*filename*

may be used.

Default: Labels are in the PRELIS command file, directly following
the LA command.

OPTION

FO   If this option appears, the variable format statement describing
the label records will appear as the next line.

Default: Labels are in free format or the format statement (if any)
is at the head of the external file containing the labels.

DETAIL LINES

(Character variable format statement)

If an external file has been specified with the FO option (or nothing
at all), and the labels are in *fixed* format, a FORTRAN A-format
statement, enclosed in parentheses, is inserted here to describe
the column assignments of the label records.

Default: the labels are in free format

Data (variable labels)

If an external file is not specified, the labels must appear at this
point in the command file.

NOTES

The number of labels entered should be equal to NI (the number of variables entered on the DA command).

If no LA command appears, the default labels for observed variables (VAR 1, VAR 2, . . .) are used. The use of real labels is recommended, however, as it makes printed output easier to read.

The order of the labels follows the order of the input variables.

There are eight columns available for labels. In free format, longer labels will be cut off at the right. In fixed format, longer labels, like (A9), will be cut off at the left. Labels shorter than eight columns will be padded with spaces to the left, in both formats.

Rules for entering labels in free format
- A label may consist of any number of characters you choose.
- If a label is longer than 8 characters, only the first 8 characters will be retained and printed by the program.
- If a label is shorter than 8 characters, it will be right-adjusted within a field of 8 characters on the printout. (Blanks will be filled-in on the left of the label if it contains fewer than eight characters, but there is no need for you to take these blanks into account when referring to labels.)
- Blanks, commas, carriage returns, and line feeds are used as delimiters.
- Blanks and commas cannot be used within a label unless the label is enclosed in single quotes.
- Line breaks are not permitted within labels.
- The return character will be ignored until all labels have been read, or until a forward slash (/) is encountered.
- If the number of labels entered is less than the number of variables you have entered (*i.e.*, if a '/' is encountered before NI number of labels have been read), the remaining variables will have the corresponding default labels.

Rules for entering labels in fixed format

A FORTRAN A-format must be specified for this option. The format statement may be up to 127 characters long. It can be specified in three different ways.

o If your labels will be entered directly in the command file, the A-format statement must come immediately after the LA command and immediately before the labels begin on the next line.

o If your labels are stored in an external file to be read by the program, you may include the A-format as the first line in that file. In this case, you need make no reference to format in the PRELIS command file itself.

o If your labels are stored in an external file to be read by the program, but that external file does not contain a format, you must enter the format in the PRELIS command file, right after the LA command.

In this case, the LA command first names the file where labels alone will be found and then specified the FO option (which signals the program that the A-format designated on the next line of the command file itself is to be used for the labels read from the external file).

See also the section *How to use FORTRAN formats* (page 38).

EXAMPLES

The following examples demonstrate the various possibilities for the LA command. Assume that the number of input variables equals eight.

```
1. LA
   'LABEL 1',, 'LABEL 3' 'LABEL 4'
   'LABEL 5', 'LABEL 6'/
```

The LA command, without anything, indicates that labels in free format will be next. The labels are separated by a comma, a space or a return character, hence the labels themselves are in right quotes (or apostrophes) to protect the space within each label. The double comma (,,) tells the program that no label will be given here and the default should be used. A triple comma (,,,) would skip two labels, etc. The forward slash (/) ends the list of labels before their number equals NI on the DA command, otherwise it is not needed. Again, default labels will be used. So, the result of example 1 would be:

```
LABEL 1    VAR 2 LABEL 3 LABEL 4 LABEL 5 LABEL 6 VAR 7 VAR 8
```

2. LA
```
   (4A7)
   LABEL 1LABEL 2LABEL 3LABEL 4
   LABEL 5LABEL 6LABEL 7LABEL 8
```

This time, a fixed format is used, informing the program that four labels of seven characters will follow. Since NI=8, two such lines are expected. In fixed format no defaults are available, of course.

3. LA FI=LABEL

No detail lines are expected after the LA command. The labels are in the external file called LABEL. If the labels are in fixed format, LABEL will start with a variable format statement, otherwise, in free format, the labels start immediately.

4. LA=LABEL FO
```
   (8A7)
```

The difference with the example above is that the FO option indicates that a format statement will follow in the command file. This format shows that the labels are in fixed format, with eight labels per record. Note also that the short form LA=LABEL is used instead of LA FI=LABEL. This is allowed with PRELIS 2.

5. LA
```
   'VIS PERC'   CUBES   LOZENGES   'PAR COMP'   'SEN COMP'   WORDMEAN
   LA
   'VIS PERC'   CUBES   LOZENGES   'PAR COMP','SEN COMP',
   WORDMEAN
   LA
   'VIS PERCEPTION'  CUBES  LOZENGES  'PAR  COMP'  'SEN  COMPLETION'
   WORDMEANING
```

These three ways to enter labels in free format are all equivalent.

PURPOSE

To specify an external file with the raw data.

FORMAT

RA   FI=*filename,filename,...* FO RE

(Variable format statement)

KEYWORD

FI

- o Raw data must be read from another file specified on the RA command with the FI keyword. With PRELIS 2, the short form RA=*filename* may be used. See the section *Merging files* on page 162 about reading in data from several external files. (See below for rules about entries in the raw data file.)
- o The data file specified must contain only raw data (with or without a specified format). It cannot contain labels or other information.
- o Cases will be read until NO observations have been read or until an end-of-file marker is encountered. (For observation patterns, see the WE command.)
- o If NO has not been specified on the DA command, or if NO = 0 has been entered, the program will determine the sample size, will print this number of cases in the output, and will use this number as NO in subsequent computations.
- o If the NO entered on the DA command is larger than the actual number of cases, the program will terminate input when an end-of-file is encountered in the data file and will use the correct case count in the computations.
- o If the NO entered on the DA command is smaller than the actual number of cases, only that number of cases will be read, regardless of how many more cases are stored in the data file.
- o Each case begins on a new line, and there must be NI (on the DA command) data values for each case.

OPTIONS

FO

This option is used when both of these conditions apply:
- A fixed FORTRAN format is used to read the data.
- The input format is given on the line immediately after the RA command.

RE

To run stacked input (*i.e.*, several problems in the same input file) based on the same raw data, one must rewind[2] the file containing the raw data after each use, *i.e.*, one must specify the RE (for rewind) option on the RA command. This was not necessary in PRELIS1 as the file containing the raw data was always rewound after each use. The reason for this change is that PRELIS 2 stores the raw data in memory whenever possible.

DETAIL LINE

(Variable format statement)

If the FO option does appear, a FORTRAN F-format statement, enclosed in parentheses, is inserted here to describe the column assignments of the observation records.

NOTES

Rules for creating files of raw data in free format

- Each case must begin on a new line (one case equals one row of the data matrix).
- PRELIS interprets all data values as floating point decimal numbers, but the decimal point may be omitted when entering data values which are integers.
- Blank spaces and commas in the raw data will be used as delimiters.
- Return characters will be ignored.

---

[2]The term *rewind* stems from 'mainframe' days when data were read from a file on tape. To process such a file again, the tape had to be rewound to the start of the file.

o Ending a case with a forward slash (/) may be used to indicate that all remaining data values for this case are the same as the corresponding data values for the previous case.

o Two consecutive commas may be used to specify that the corresponding data value for the previous case should be inserted between the commas; three consecutive commas imply that two data values from the previous case will be inserted; etc.

o Repetitions of the same data value can be specified with an asterisk (*) preceded by a repeat factor. For example, 4*1 means 1 1 1 1 .

Rules for creating files of raw data in user-specified format

o In the data file, enter the format first, beginning with a left parenthesis and ending with a right parenthesis. After the format, enter the raw data with each case strictly following the format.

o The format may be up to 5 lines of 127 characters each.

o The format for each data value must be a FORTRAN F-, E-, or D-format for floating point decimal numbers. (Consult a FORTRAN manual for ways formats are specified.)

o If no format is included in the external raw data file specified on the RA command, the FO option must be entered on the RA command to tell PRELIS that a format will be entered on the next line.

See also the section *How to use FORTRAN formats* (page 38).

EXAMPLE

The files PANUSA1.RAW and PANUSA2.RAW contain six variables. The first file contains the data collected at the first occasion and the second file contains the data collected at the second occasion. Both files contain data on 933 cases. The following command file will read the data from both files and store the data on all 12 variables in a new file PANUSA.RAW.

```
EXAMPLE 8: Merging two Files
DA NI=6,6
LA
NOSAY1 VOTING1 COMPLEX1 NOCARE1 TOUCH1 INTERES1
NOSAY2 VOTING2 COMPLEX2 NOCARE2 TOUCH2 INTERES2
RA=PANUSA1.RAW,PANUSA2.RAW FO
```

```
(6F1.0)
(6F1.0)
OU RA=PANUSA.RAW WI=1 ND=0
```

Note that two formats must follow the FO option on the RA command, and each must begin on a new line.

PURPOSE

To declare the scale type of variables (see also section *Type of variables* in Chapter 1).

FORMAT

OR	*varlist* ALL
CO	*varlist* ALL
CA	*varlist* ALL
CB	*varlist* ALL
CE	*varlist* ALL
FI	*varlist*

COMMAND NAMES

OR (ordinal) and
CO (continous)

Classification of variables into ordinal and continuous is done as follows:

o At the start, all variables with less than 16 distinct values (not counting missing values) in the data set are regarded as ordinal. All other variables will be treated as continuous.

o Specifications made with CO, CA, CB, CE, or OR commands can override this automatic classification.

o However, because PRELIS provides a maximum number of 15 distinct values for ordinal variables, a variable declared ordinal with an OR command that has more than 15 distinct (not counting missing values) values in the data set, after possible recoding and transformation, will be treated as continuous.

CA (censored above),

CB (censored below), and

CE (censored above and below)

Censored variables must be explicitly declared by CA, CB, or CE commands. After the maximum or minimum value of the censored variables has been replaced by its corresponding normal score, these variables are treated as continuous variables.

FI (fixed)

To specify x-variables. See page 178 in Appendix B for details.

SPECIFICATIONS

varlist

is a list of variables identified by labels or numbers. Alternatively, ALL may be entered to indicate a recoding that applies to all variables in the data. See page 60 for examples.

EXAMPLES

Note: in the following illustrations, we use OR commands, but the examples apply as well to CO, CA, CB, CE, and FI commands.

To declare variables 2, 4, 7, and 11 to be ordinal, enter:

    OR 2 4 7, 11

Using labels for these variables instead, the same specification could be entered as:

    OR CUBES 'PAR COMP' ADDITION, 'VAR 11'

Apostrophes are necessary only when labels contain blanks, commas, or slashes. Blanks and commas are delimiters and may be used interchangeably. Labels and numbers can be mixed. This example could, therefore, be entered as:

    OR 2, 'PAR COMP' 3 'VAR 11'

Consecutive variables may be specified using a hyphen or minus sign. For example, to declare variables 2, 3, 4, 5, 7, 9, 10, and 11 to be ordinal, enter:

    OR 2-5 7 9-11

These variables could also be specified to be ordinal using labels and hyphens, such as:

```
OR CUBES-'SEN COMP' ADDITION 'S-C CAPS'- 'VAR 11'
```

The following will also work (blanks before and after the hyphen are ignored):

```
OR 2 -'SEN COMP' 7 'S-C CAPS'- 11
```

The following command may be used to specify that all variables are ordinal:

```
OR ALL
```

PURPOSE

o To transform ordinal variables into other ordinal variables with fewer categories.

o To convert a continous variable to an ordinal variable.

o To recode values to the missing value, so that some real observations will be treated as missing observations.

o To combine (collapse) several categories to form a new category.

o To redefine the order of categories.

FORMAT

RE | $varlist$
 ALL | OLD=$valuerange,valuerange,...$

                       NEW=$value,value,...$

SPECIFICATIONS

varlist

is a list of variables identified by labels or numbers. Alternatively, ALL may be entered to indicate a recoding that applies to all variables in the data. See page 60 for examples.

OLD=*valuerange*

Specifies the existing data value(s) that you want to recode. *valuerange* is either a single value or a range of values of the form $v_1 - v_2$, where v_1 and v_2 are two numeric values with $v_1 \leq v_2$. PRELIS 2 allows a list of *valueranges*, separated with commas.

NEW=*value*

Specifies the value(s) replacing the one(s) listed with OLD. *value* is a numeric value, with or without a decimal point. PRELIS 2 allows a list of *values*, separated with commas. Naturally, this list should have the same number of elements as the list of *valueranges*.

NOTES

See also the section *Improvement of the recode command* in Appendix B (p. 150).

OLD and NEW keywords must be given exactly as specified: with equal signs, without blanks. The characters may be upper or lower case, so long as the two cases are not mixed. Make sure that no label is identical to the keywords.

EXAMPLES

Example 1

Suppose variables 11–14 are on five-category scales. These can all be dichotomized by letting categories 1, 2, and 3, say, form a new category 0, and categories 4 and 5 form a new category 1. This is done with the RE command:

```
RECODE 11-14 OLD=1-3,4-5 NEW=0,1
```

Example 2

Although the RE command is primarily intended for transforming ordinal variables, it can also be used to transform continuous variables.

Suppose that the continuous variable labeled XVAR has scores in the range 0–100. This can be transformed into another variable with scores 1, 2, ..., 5 with the RE command:

```
RECODE XVAR OLD=0-45,46-60,61-70,71-80,81-100 NEW=1,2,3,4,5
```

If XVAR is declared ordinal, the recoded variable will also be ordinal. If XVAR is declared continuous, the recoded XVAR will also be continuous. But if the recoded XVAR has less than sixteen distinct values, the recoded XVAR will be ordinal.

Example 3

The six efficacy items in Example 7B go from high agreement to low agreement, since *1 = Agree Strongly* and *4 = Disagree Strongly*. Suppose we wish to change the scale so that it goes from low to high.

```
RE NOSAY - INTEREST OLD=1,2,3,4 NEW=4,3,2,1
```

Suppose, we wish to dichotomize the variables by collapsing the two agree categories and the two disagree categories and at the same time recode the scale so that it goes from low to high. This can be done simply as:

```
RE NOSAY - INTEREST OLD=1-2,3-4 NEW=1,0
```

After this recoding, *0 = disagree* and *1 = agree*.

PURPOSE
To assign labels to the categories of ordinal variables.

FORMAT

CL $\quad$ | $varlist$ | n_1=*clab*$_1$ $\quad$ n_2=*clab*$_2$ ...
$\qquad$ | ALL |

SPECIFICATIONS

varlist

> is a list of variables identified by labels or numbers. The option ALL may be used instead to indicate that all variables will have these category labels. See page 60 for examples.

$n_1, n_2, \ldots$

> are the numerical values in the data on these variables.

clab$_1$, *clab*$_2$, ...

> are the labels to be assigned to these numerical values.
> Each category label may contain up to four characters.

NOTES

See also the section *Labels for categories* (p. 147) in Appendix B.

Each CL command contains a *varlist* listing all variables with the same category labels, followed by a listing defining category labels for numerical values. If the category labels do not fit on a line of 127 characters, repeat the same CL command and *varlist* and continue with the remaining category labels. If the *varlist* on the CL command is too long to fit on one line of 127 characters, write the remaining variables in *varlist* on a new CL command followed by the same list of category labels as for the previous CL command.

Important: If some of the variables are recoded, the category labels refer to the recoded values.

EXAMPLE

The following command file will read the six political efficacy items from the file EX7.RAW and assign category labels AS, A, D, DS, DK, and NA to the numerical values 1, 2, 3, 4, 8, and 9, respectively (AS = *Agree Strongly*, A = *Agree*, D = *Disagree*, DS = *Disagree Strongly*, DK = *Don't Know*, NA = *No Answer*).

```
EXAMPLE 7B
!Assigning Category Labels as follows
!AS = Agree Strongly, A = Agree, D = Disagree, DS = Disagree Strongly,
!DK = Don't Know, NA = No Answer
DA NI=6
LA;NOSAY VOTING COMPLEX NOCARE TOUCH INTEREST  ! Note the ;
RA=EX7.RAW FO;(141X,6F2.0)                      ! Note the ;
CL NOSAY - INTEREST 1=AS 2=A 3=D 4=DS 8=DK 9=NA
OU
```

Note that one must know which numerical values are present in the data to do this.

Define a new variableNE

PURPOSE
To create a new variable as a function of existing variables.

FORMAT

NE   *newvar=function of old variables, NRAND and/or URAND*

SPECIFICATIONS

newvar

>is the label for the new variable. If *newvar* is an already existing label, the new variable replaces the old. A separate NE command is used to define each new variable.

function of old variables

>The formula defining the new variable is written in a straightforward way. These are the rules:

>o   Multiplication is specified with *.
>o   Exponentiation is specified with ** or ^.
>o   Parentheses are not permitted, but this is no restriction because new variables can be functions of other new variables already defined.
>o   Division is not permitted, although exponents may be negative.
>o   Constants are written as usual. If they are written without a decimal point, they are taken to be integers.

>The new variables will be computed for each case in the data. If any of the variables $x_1, x_2, \ldots, x_k$ defining the new variable is missing for a case, the value of the new variable will be missing for this case.

NRAND and URAND

>NRAND generates a random normal variable with mean zero and variance one. URAND generates a uniform random variable over the interval (0,1). Each time NRAND or URAND is specified in the command file, a new random normal variable independent of previously generated variables, is generated.

EXAMPLES

Example 1

```
NE var5=2.5*var1+var2-var3
NE var4=var4-var2
NE var6=var1**2
NE var7=var1*var2
NE var8=var1+var2*var3-var2**2
NE var8=var8**2
```

The last two commands illustrate how one can define var8 as the square of a quadratic expression.

Example 2

New variables can also be transformed by power or log transformations or recoded. For example, if x is a defined variable, one may define two new variables $y_1 = \sqrt{1 + x^2}$ and $y_2 = \log{(1 + x^2)}$ with the commands:

```
NE Y1=1+X**2
NE Y2=1+X**2
PO Y1 GA=.5
LO Y2
```

Example 3

Two new variables Efficacy and Respons are created as a linear combination of the original variables. The keyword NI specified on the DA command will be increased by one for each NE command defining a *new* label so that the new variables will automatically be included in the analysis.

```
! EXAMPLE 7F: Computing Scale Scores
DA NI=6
LA; NOSAY VOTING COMPLEX NOCARE TOUCH INTEREST
RA=EFFICACY.RAW FO; (6F1.0)
NEW EFFICACY = NOSAY + VOTING + COMPLEX
NEW RESPONS = NOCARE + TOUCH + INTEREST
OU MA=PM WP
```

Example 4

In PRELIS, the random variables NRAND and URAND act as ordinary variables, except they are not read from a raw data file. They can be combined with other variables which have been read from a file or have been generated previously. As the following examples demonstrate, there are almost unlimited possibilities of generating normal and non-normal variables with specified properties.

Using the RE (recode) command one can also generate discrete variables (ordinal or categorical).

The following command file generates 200 independent cases of six variables having a multivariate normal distribution with zero mean vector and covariance matrix Σ. Note that there is no NI value specified on the DA command.

```
! Generating multivariate normal variables
! with a specified covariance matrix
DA NO=200
NE V1=NRAND; NE V2=NRAND; NE V3=NRAND
NE V4=NRAND; NE V5=NRAND; NE V6=NRAND
NE X1=V1
NE X2=.378*V1+.925806*V2
NE X3=.72*V1+.068956*V2+.690540*V3
NE X4=.324*V1+.321372*V2+.047151*V3+.88855*V4
NE X5=.27*V1+.26781*V2+.039292*V3+.140229*V4+.913329*V5
NE X6=.27*V1+.025858*V2+.063453*V3+.010374*V4+.006818*V5+.960339*V6
CO ALL
SD V1-V6
OU RA=RAWDATA WI=7 ND=3 XM IX=123456
```

Here we generate data on V1 through V6 which are independent and normally distributed with mean zero and variance one. V1 through V6 are then transformed linearly to X1 through X6 using the $\mathbf{T}$ matrix. After X1 through X6 have been defined, V1 through V6 can be deleted. This is done with the SD command.

See Appendix C for more details and examples.

PURPOSE

To specify certain variables to be transformed before the requested moment matrix is computed.

FORMAT

PO   *varlist* AL= | **0** / α-*value*   BE= | **1** / β-*value*   GA= | **1** / γ-*value*

LO   *varlist* AL= | **0** / α-*value*   BE= | **1** / β-*value*

SPECIFICATIONS

varlist

is a list of variables identified by labels or numbers. See page 60 for examples.

α-*value*, β-*value*, and γ-*value*

are any values of α, β, and γ for which the transformation is defined.

Default: AL=0, BE=1, GA=1

NOTES

All selections and computations, including data screening, will be based on the transformed variables. The transformations can be used to approximate normal distribution characteristics of the variables. Any transformation in a general family may be used. This family of transformations is defined by:

$$y = (\alpha + \beta x)^{\gamma} \text{ (PO)}$$
$$y = \log(\alpha + \beta x) \text{ (LO)}$$

where x is the untransformed variable and y is the transformed variable.

Each choice of α, β, and γ defines a particular transformation in this family. For example:

$\gamma = 2$ gives a square transformation
$\gamma = 1/2$ gives a square root transformation
$\gamma = -1$ gives an inverse transformation

LO gives a logarithmic transformation.

Some care must be exercised when transforming variables, because there may be values of α, β, and γ for which the transformation is not defined for all values of x in the data. For example, when $\gamma = 1/2$, $(\alpha + \beta x)$ must be non-negative for all observed values of x. With LO, all values of $(\alpha + \beta x)$ must be positive. Failure to observe this will result in warning message 207 and fatal error message 303 (see Appendix A).

The PO and LO commands imply that all variables specified by *varlist* will be transformed with the same transformation. If other variables should be transformed by some other transformation, this must be specified on another PO or LO command. Any number of such commands may be included in the command file.

PO and LO commands are intended to transform continuous variables. The program will also transform ordinal and censored variables, if requested, but this would not usually be meaningful. For transformation of ordinal variables, see the RE command (page 62).

PURPOSE

To generate a subsample of the total sample.

FORMAT

SC   *varlist conditionlist*

SC   CASE=*condition*

SPECIFICATIONS

varlist

> is a list of variables identified by labels or numbers. See page 60 for examples.

conditionlist

> is a list of conditions of the form (a, b, and c are numeric values):
>
> $< a$ (less than a)
> $> b$ (larger than b)
> $= c$ (equal to c)

CASE=*condition*

> where *condition* is one of four possibilities (d is a whole number):
>
> ODD   Selects all odd-numbered cases from the dataset
> EVEN   Selects all even-numbered cases from the dataset
> $< d$ Selects all cases before case d from the dataset
> $> d$ Selects all cases after case d from the dataset

NOTES

Either or both of the formats given for the SC command may be used several times in the command file, if needed. *Only the selected cases will be used in the analysis.*

The *first form* of the SC command generates a subsample of the total sample (a subset of rows of the data matrix) by selecting cases which satisfy certain conditions on certain variables. The following rules apply:

- The SC command selects those cases for which all the conditions in the *conditionlist* are satisfied in all the variables in the *varlist*.

- To have one set of conditions apply to one set of variables, and another set of conditions apply to another set of variables, use two SC commands.
- SC commands do not reduce the number of variables.
- All variables will be used in the analysis, including those on which the selection is based.
- To reduce the number of variables, one can use SD commands to select variables to be deleted from analysis (see page 75).
- If the selection is based on a variable or several variables which have been transformed with PO or LO commands, or which have been recoded with RE commands, the selection will be made on the transformed variable(s). It is not possible to select values on one variable and then transform those values. The transformation will always be done first and then the selection. This holds regardless of the order of the SC, SD, PO, LO, and RE commands in the command file.

The *second form* of the SC command generates a subsample of the total sample by selecting cases directly.

This form is useful, for example, to select a random subsample of cases to be used for exploration versus cross-validation or other studies of sampling variability (see Jöreskog & Aish, 1996). A random subsample of any size can also be obtained by bootstrap sampling (see the section *Bootstrap estimates*, p. 171, in Appendix B).

EXAMPLES

Suppose variables 2, 7, 8, 9, 10, and 11 have integer scores in the range of 1–5.

    SC 2 7-11 = 2

selects all cases which have a score of 2 on all of the variables 2, 7–11.

    SC 2 7-11 < 3

selects all cases with scores less than 3.

    SC 2, 7-11 > 1 < 4

selects all cases with scores between 1 and 4; *i.e.*, all cases with scores 2 or 3.

```
SC 2, 7-11 < 3 > 4
```
selects no cases, because both conditions cannot be true.

The two forms of the SC command can be used in combination as follows:

```
SC CASE=condition
SC varlist conditionlist
```

This selects all cases which satisfy *both* the *condition* for the cases *and all* conditions in the *conditionlist* for the variables in *varlist*. Only these selected cases will be used in the analysis. For example, if GENDER is coded 1 for males and 2 for females,

```
SC case=odd
SC GENDER =2
```

will select all females with odd case numbers (note the space between GENDER (the *varlist*) and =2 (the *conditionlist*).

PURPOSE

To generate a subsample of the total sample and exclude variables from the analysis.

FORMAT

SD   *varlist conditionlist*

SPECIFICATIONS

varlist

is a list of variables identified by labels or numbers. See page 60 for examples.

conditionlist

is a list of conditions of the forms (a, b, and c are numeric values):

$< a$ (less than a)
$> b$ (larger than b)
$= c$ (equal to c)

NOTES

Unlike the SE command in LISREL, which marks variables to be included in the analysis, the SD command in PRELIS marks variables to be excluded from analysis.

The SD command has the same function and the same syntax as the SC command, with one difference.

o First, cases will be selected on the basis of *varlist* and *conditionlist*.
o Then — and here is the difference — the variables in *varlist* on which the selection is based will be deleted from further consideration.
o The analysis will be based on a subset of the cases and a subset of the variables.

By choosing an empty *conditionlist* (so that all cases satisfy all conditions), one can exclude variables from the analysis without selecting any cases. The program automatically reduces the value of NI by the number of variables in the *varlist*.

EXAMPLES

Example 1

Suppose the data include the variable SEX with scores 0 for males and 1 for females.

To do an analysis of the females only, use

```
SD SEX=1
```

SD works better than SC here, because SC would result in data where the variable SEX is included, but all cases in the selected subsample would have the value 1 on this variable. With SD, this variable will not be included in the analysis. (Variables on which all cases have the same value, would not be useful for any purpose, of course, and will lead to fatal errors if correlations are requested. See Appendix A.)

Example 2

Suppose the raw data contain 30 variables, but only the first 14 are to be used in the analysis.

This can be done with an SD command by entering *varlist* only:

```
SD 15-30
```

No conditions are given, so all cases will be selected.
After the selection, the variables 15–30 are discarded.

PURPOSE

To substitute missing values in the data with real values through imputation.

FORMAT

IM   *(Ivarlist) (Mvarlist)   VR=* **0.5** *XN XL*
                                        value

SPECIFICATIONS

(Ivarlist)

is a set of variables whose missing values should be imputed.

(Mvarlist)

is a set of matching variables.

See page 60 for examples on how to specify a *varlist*.

KEYWORD

VR   A cutoff criterion (variance ratio; explained in the section *Imputation of missing values* on page 153), below which *no* imputation will be done.
Larger values than the default (0.5) are not recommended. Use smaller values to increase the precision in the imputation.
Default: 0.5

OPTIONS

XN   list only successful imputations

XL   skip the entire listing of cases

NOTES

See also the sections *Specification of missing values* (p. 152) and *Imputation of missing values* (p. 153) in Appendix B.

PRELIS offers three ways of handling missing values: pairwise deletion, listwise deletion, and imputation. See the DA command on page 48 for the first two.

Imputation is the substitution of real values for missing values. The value to be substituted for the missing value for a case is obtained from another case that has a similar response pattern over a set of matching variables.

If *Ivarlist* contains several variables, they will be imputed in the order they are listed. This is of no consequence if no variables in *Ivarlist* are included in *Mvarlist*. Ideally, *Ivarlist* contains the variables with missing values and *Mvarlist* contains variables without missing values. However, PRELIS can handle also the case when some variables are included in both *varlists* and, in fact, the two *varlists* could be identical.

If a variable is included in both *varlists*, it is automatically excluded from *Mvarlist* when its values are imputed. In this case, the order of the variables in *Ivarlist* can make a difference, since a variable already imputed can be used as matching variable when another variable is imputed.

Imputation of missing values should be done with utmost care and control, since missing values will be replaced by other values that will be treated as real observed values. If possible, use matching variables which are *not* to be used in the LISREL modeling. Otherwise, if the matching variables are included in the LISREL model, it is likely that the imputation will affect the result of analysis. This should be checked by comparing with the result obtained without imputation.

For each variable to be imputed, PRELIS lists all the cases with missing values. If imputation is successful, it gives the value imputed, the number of matching cases and the variance ratio. If the imputation is not successful, it gives the reason for the failure. This can be either that no matching case was found or that the variance ratio was too large. PRELIS always gives the number of missing values per variable, both before and after imputation.

Important: Imputation is done after all recodings and other data transformations (see the section *Order of computations*, p. 164 in Appendix B).
If it is required to do recodings or other transformation on the imputed data, one can do this by running PRELIS twice. In the first run, do the imputation and save the raw data (see the section *Saving the raw data*, p. 159 in Appendix B). In the second run, use the saved raw data after imputation and do the recodings or other transformations.

Treatment of missing values is done after all data manipulations. If imputation is requested, this is done first. If TR is default or if TR=LI on the DA
command, all cases with missing values remaining after imputation will
be eliminated and all further computations will be based on the listwise
sample. If TR=PA on the DA command, no deletion of cases will be made
in the raw data.

EXAMPLE

In the following command file, missing values on each variable are imputed using all the other variables as matching variables. Cases with
missing values are eliminated after imputation. Category labels are then
assigned to the data values that remain after listwise deletion and the data
screening is done on this subsample.

```
EXAMPLE 7D
Imputing Missing Values
DA NI=6 MI=8,9
LA;NOSAY VOTING COMPLEX NOCARE TOUCH INTEREST
RA FI=EX7.RAW FO;(141X,6F2.0)
IM (NOSAY - INTEREST) (NOSAY - INTEREST)
CL  NOSAY - INTEREST 1=AS 2=A 3=D 4=DS
OU
```

PURPOSE

To designate one or more numbers used to represent missing values in a subset of variables.

FORMAT

MI   *value,value,... varlist*

SPECIFICATIONS

value

is any number (with or without a decimal point) used to represent missing values. Whenever a number equal to this value is found in the raw data for any of the listed variables, it will be treated as a missing observation.

If more than one *value* is given, separate the elements in the list with commas.

Instead of each single value, a range of values may be used.

varlist

is a list of variables identified by labels or numbers. See page 60 for examples.

NOTES

See also the sections *Specification of missing values* (p. 152) and *Imputation of missing values* (p. 153) in Appendix B.

All missing value representations must be specified by MI commands if:

- o There are missing observations in the data.
- o Different variables have different missing value representations.
- o No global MI value has been specified on the DA command for all missing observations.

Treatment of missing values is done after all data manipulations. If imputation is requested, this is done first. If TR is default or if TR=LI on the DA command, all cases with missing values remaining after imputation will be eliminated and all further computations will be based on the listwise sample. If TR=PA on the DA command, no deletion of cases will be made in the raw data.

EXAMPLES

Note: in the examples below, we have used integers to represent variables in the varlist. Labels could have been used instead.

Example 1

To use 0 to represent missing observations in variables 2, 3, 4, 5, 8, 9, 10, and 11; and -9 to represent missing observations in variables 1 and 7:

```
MISSING-VALUE 0 2-5 8-11
MISSING-VALUE -9 1,7
```

Example 2

The specification made on an MI command overrides the global specification made by the MI value on the DA command:

```
DA ... MI = -99
MISSING-VALUE 0,-9 3 7 9
```

This indicates 0 and -9 represent missing values in variables 3, 7, and 9; but -99 represents missing values in all other variables.

Example 3

A missing value representation specified on one MI command may override what has been specified on a previous MI command:

```
RAW-DATA ... MI = -99
MISSING-VALUE -9 2-9
MISSING-VALUE 0-1,8 3 6
```

These commands say that values from 0 to 1, inclusive, as well as 8 represent missing values in variables 3 and 6; -9 represents missing values in variables 2, 4, 5, 7, 8, and 9 (*not* 3 and 6); and -99 represents missing values in all other variables.

PURPOSE

To define one variable as a weight-variable.

FORMAT

WE   *variable*

Default: When there is no WE command in the command file, the program
treats all cases as single cases.

NOTES

○ One variable is defined (either by an integer or by a label) as a
'weight variable' whose values are integers n_i specifying that 'the
i-th case' is to be counted n_i times. This can be used to analyze
grouped data or data from probability samples where units in the
population have different probabililties of appearing in the sample.

○ Any of the NI input variables may be declared to be a weight-variable in this way (it does not have to be the first or the last of the
input variables). Note that the value NI specified on the DA command
should include the weight-variable.

○ Values of the weight-variable in the raw data must be values that
sum to the total sample size specified with NO on the DA command.
In most applications, these values are integers representing repeat
factors (each case is to be counted a certain number of times), but
the program will also allow real values (with decimal points) representing more general weights. After all the PRELIS control lines have
been read and interpreted, PRELIS reduces the value of NI by 1, and
separates the weight variable from the other variables.

○ When a WE command is present in the command file, the program
treats all cases (rows of the data matrix) as patterns of observations
and finds the frequency of each pattern in the variable (column of
the data matrix) designated as the weight-variable.

EXAMPLES

Note: In the examples below, we assume that the weight-variable (in these examples, the first variable) has been given the label FREQUENCY.

o Data on two dichotomous variables in the form of a 2×2 contingency table

	0	1
0	24	76
1	93	144

may be input to PRELIS with the command WE FREQUENCY in the form of the following raw data.

```
 24    0    0
 76    0    1
 93    1    0
144    1    1
```

o Data presented in the following form:

Age in years	Response to Question					Total
	5	4	3	2	1	
5	0	0	2	0	1	3
6	0	0	0	1	3	4
7	0	1	0	3	0	4
8	1	1	3	1	0	6
9	0	2	3	2	2	9
10	0	2	7	6	0	15
11	0	2	2	6	1	11
12	2	0	2	5	5	14
13	0	1	2	5	4	12
14	1	3	3	2	0	9
15	1	2	3	2	0	8
Totals	5	14	27	33	16	95

may be input to PRELIS with the command WE FREQUENCY in the form of the following raw data.

```
2    3    5
1    1    5
1    2    6
3    1    6
```

etc.

PURPOSE

To test the homogeneity of pairs of nominal or ordinal variables.

FORMAT

HT   *varlist*

SPECIFICATIONS

varlist

is a list of variables identified by labels or numbers. See page 60 for examples.

NOTES

See the section *Homogeneity tests for categorical variables* on p. 173 in Appendix B.

Some matrix must be specified on the OU command to make the program compute all the bivariate marginal contingency tables that are needed for the calculation of the test statistics. Any matrix appropriate for ordinal variables will do, that is, OM, PM, RM, or TM.

With ordinal variables, PRELIS gives a bivariate contingency table for each pair of variables, both in absolute frequencies and in percentages. With 12 variables, for example, there will be 66 such tables of each kind. One can put the XB option on the OU command to skip the printing of these tables in the output file.

PURPOSE

To estimate common thresholds for ordinal variables.

FORMAT

ET   *varlist*

SPECIFICATIONS

varlist

is a list of variables identified by labels or numbers. See page 60 for examples.

NOTES

See *Thresholds* on page 176 in Appendix B.

This command will make PRELIS estimate the thresholds under the condition that they are *equal* for all ordinal variables in *varlist*.

A test of equal thresholds can be obtained by running PRELIS 2 with and without the ET command and computing the difference in chi-squares for each polychoric correlation.

PURPOSE

To read fixed thresholds for ordinal variables from an external file.

FORMAT

FT   FI=*filename* | *varlist1* |
                                 | ALL |

FT   *varlist2*

FT   *varlist3*

. . .

. . .

SPECIFICATIONS

filename

> specifies the file where the fixed thresholds are to be read.
> The shorter form, FT=*filename* may also be used.

varlist1, *varlist2*, etc.

> are lists of variables identified by labels or numbers. See page 60 for examples. Alternatively, the option ALL may be entered to select all the variables in the analysis.

NOTE

Only the first in a series of FT commands specifies the external file with the thresholds. The first line in this file contains the thresholds that will be assigned to the variables in *varlist1*. The thresholds in the second line in the file will be assigned to the variables in *varlist2*, etc. In most applications, each *varlist* will contain only one variable.

EXAMPLE

The following two FT commands

```
FT=THRESH X2 X4 X5
FT X1 X3
```

will set the thresholds equal for variables X2, X4, and X5 and read the values for these thresholds from the first line in the file THRESH, and then set the thresholds equal for variables X1 and X3 and read the values for these thresholds from the second line in the file THRESH.

PURPOSE

To estimate thresholds for ordinal variables from their marginal distributions.

FORMAT

MT | *varlist* |
             | ALL |

SPECIFICATIONS

varlist

is a list of variables identified by labels or numbers. See page 60 for examples.

NOTES

See page 178 in Appendix B for details.

The use of this command causes the thresholds to be estimated from the marginal distributions of the ordinal variables in *varlist*. The regression coefficients in the probit regressions are then estimated for fixed thresholds.

PURPOSE

To estimate the regression of any variable on any set of variables.

FORMAT

RG | *y-varlist* | ON | *x-varlist* |
       | *ALL* | | *ALL* |

SPECIFICATIONS

x-varlist and *y-varlist*

are lists of variables identified by labels or numbers. See p. 60 for examples.

The word ON must appear between the *varlists*.

The option ALL may be used instead of *x-varlist* or *y-varlist* or both.

NOTES

The RG command makes it possible to estimate the regression of any variable on any set of variables, to explore data further so that a suitable LISREL model may be specified (especially useful for submodel 2).

- Each variable in the *y-varlist* will be regressed on all variables in the *x-varlist*.
- Some variables may be included in both *varlists*, but the program never regresses a variable on itself.
- For each regression, the program automatically excludes the left-hand *y* variable from the *x* variables, if this is included in the *x-varlist*.
- Up to ten RG commands may be given for each problem.

For each regression, the program gives the following quantities:

- estimated regression coefficients based on the moment matrix requested with the MA keyword:

  MA=KM, OM, or PM — the regression coefficients will be standardized

  MA=CM — the regression coefficients will be unstandardized

  MA=AM — an intercept term will appear as the coefficient of the constant variable'

o standard errors of the estimated regression coefficient
o t-values of the estimated regression coefficients
o residual variance
o squared multiple correlation

The computed and reported standard errors and t-values are based on the classical normality assumption, even when this assumption is not valid. Interpret the standard errors and t-values with caution. See also page 166 in Appendix B.

EXAMPLES

```
RG 1 2 3 ON ALL
```

will regress each of the variables 1, 2, and 3 on all the other variables.

```
RG ALL ON ALL
```

will regress each variable on all the others (Guttman's, 1953, image analysis).

PURPOSE

To control list output and to save results in external files.

FORMAT

OU	MA=	AM		RA=*filename*		AC=*filename*
		CM		SR=*filename*		SA=*filename*
		KM				
		MM				
		OM				
		PM				
		RM				
		TM				

AM=*filename* CM=*filename* KM=*filename* MM=*filename*

OM=*filename* PM=*filename* RM=*filename* TM=*filename*

SM=*filename* SV=*filename* TH=*filename*

BM=*filename* ME=*filename* SD=*filename*

BS=*no. of bootstrap samples* SF=*sample fraction*

IX=*integer starting value for the random number generator*

WI=*format width* ND=*no. of decimals*

PA PV PK WP XB XT XM

KEYWORDS

MA   Type of moment matrix to be estimated:

AM   augmented moment matrix

CM   covariance matrix

KM   matrix of product moment (Pearson) correlations

MM   matrix of moments about zero

OM   matrix of correlations based on optimal scores

PM   matrix of product moment (Pearson), polychoric, and poly-serial correlations

RM   matrix of Spearman rank correlations

TM   matrix of Kendall's tau-c correlations

Default: If MA is not specified, no moment matrix will be estimated; only univariate data screening will be performed.

SM   specifies the *filename* where the estimated moment matrix, specified with MA, will be saved.

AM, CM, KM, MM, OM, PM, RM, TM
Alternatively, instead of SM one can use the same matrix name as specified with the MA keyword to save the moment matrix.

SR or RA
specifies the *filename* where the transformed raw data will be saved.

SA or AC
specifies the *filename* where the asymptotic covariance matrix of the estimated variances, covariances, or correlations will be saved. This may be used with the WLS method in LISREL. Note that this file is saved in binary format (see page 167 in Appendix B).

SV   specifies the *filename* where the asymptotic variances of the estimated variances, covariances, or correlations will be saved. This may be used with the DWLS method in LISREL.

TH   specifies the *filename* where the common thresholds will be saved. These common thresholds are then subsequently read with the FT command (see page 87).
See the section Thresholds on page 176 in Appendix B for further explanation.

BM   specifies the *filename* where all the *MA*-matrices computed for each bootstrap sample will be saved.

ME   specifies the *filename* where all the mean vectors computed for each bootstrap sample will be saved.

SD   specifies the *filename* where all the standard deviations computed for each bootstrap sample will be saved.

See Appendix C for bootstrapping procedures.

Default: none.

Data and results will not be saved, unless one or more of the *filenames* are specified with the appropriate keyword.

BS   specifies the number of bootstrap samples to be generated

SF   specifies the sample fraction of each sample as a percentage. If the raw data file has 296 observations and SF=50, each bootstrap sample will be of size 148.

IX   specifies the integer starting value for the random number generator.

For both bootstrapping and Monte Carlo experimenting, PRELIS uses a random number generator of Schrage (1979) to generate uniform random numbers in double precision. This requires a seed as a starting number for the generator. The seed may be specified as IX=i, where i is a random integer.

If IX is not specified, its value will be set equal to the number of seconds passed since last midnight. In this case, this means that if two persons run the same command file or if one person runs the same command file at different times, the two runs will not produce the same result, although the two results represent realizations of the same random phenomenon. To reproduce exactly the same result, one must explicitly specify the seed with the IX keyword.

WI   specifies the width of each field for the raw data file saved with the RA or SR keyword.

ND   specifies the number of decimals in each field for the raw data file saved with the RA or SR keyword.

For example, the command OU RA=RAWDATA WI=7 ND=3 will save the raw data in the file RAWDATA in the format 6F7.3. See also Example 4 below.

OPTIONS

PA   If SA has *also* been specified, the asymptotic covariance matrix will be printed in the list output.

PV   If SV has *also* been specified, the asymptotic variances will be printed in the list output.

Do not use PA or PV when several vectors of asymptotic estimates are stacked in the same file. To save computer memory, the vector of asymptotic estimates requested with SA=filename PA or SV=file-name PV is computed and written to the file in sections. Only one section of the vector exists in memory at any one time. When PA or PV is requested, all the workspace is devoted to reading the file into memory and producing printed versions of the vector in the output file. This is why PA cannot be executed without SA; and why PV cannot be executed without SV.

Also note that there is a scale factor difference between the printed asymptotic covariance matrix and the matrix written to the file. The printed matrix is correct. The entries in the saved matrix are multiplied by the sample size, as required by LISREL 7. Note that this file is saved in binary format (see page 167 in Appendix B).

WP   If given, printed output will be 132 columns wide.

Default: 80 columns wide

XB   If given, bivariate frequency tables will *not* be printed in the list output.

Default: bivariate frequency tables will be printed

XT   If given, test statistics will *not* be printed in the list output.

Default: test statistics will be printed

Bivariate tables and test statistics are included in the standard output when MA=PM. These tables may contain important information, and most users will want to inspect them. However, when the number of variables becomes large, bivariate frequency tables and test statistics will create a very large output file. XB and XT options are provided to shorten the output file, should this information be unnecessary.

XM   If given, the tests of multivariate normality will *not* be computed. Because these tests are rather time consuming, this option allows to skip those computations (and output listings).

Default: test will be computed and listed in the output

NOTES

The MM, AM, CM, and KM moment matrices are based on raw scores or on transformed scores for those variables that have been transformed with PO, LO, and/or RE commands. Ordinal variables present after these transformations, if any, will be transformed to normal scores before the moment matrix is computed. Similarly, for censored variables, the maximum and minimum scores will be transformed to normal scores before the moment matrix is computed.

AM is an augmented moment matrix. Suppose one reads NI$=k$ and MA=AM on the OU command. The program will compute the augmented moment matrix M of order $(k+1) \times (k+1)$, defined as:

$$\begin{bmatrix} m_{11} & & & \\ m_{21} & m_{22} & & \\ \vdots & \vdots & \ddots & \\ m_{k1} & m_{k2} & \cdots & m_{kk} \\ \bar{z}_1 & \bar{z}_2 & \cdots & \bar{z}_k & 1, \end{bmatrix}$$

where the m_{ij} are the moments about zero, and the $\bar{z}_i$ are the means of the input variables. This is the sample moment matrix when the variable 'const,' equal to one for every case, has been added as the last variable. This variable will be given the default label CONST. The program also automatically updates NI from NI$=k$ to NI$=k+1$.

The augmented moment matrix is needed in LISREL whenever the model involves constant intercept terms and/or mean values of latent variables.

OM is a matrix of correlations based on optimal scores. It may contain different kinds of correlations for each pair of variables.

If both variables in the pair are continuous, the correlation is an ordinary product moment (Pearson) correlation. If one variable is continuous and the other is ordinal, the correlation is a simple consistent estimate of the polyserial correlation (see Jöreskog, 1986). If both variables are ordinal, the correlation is the canonical correlation (see Kendall & Stuart, 1961, pp. 568–573).

PM is a matrix of product-moment (Pearson) correlations, polychoric correlations, and/or polyserial correlations

- o The product-moment correlation is a correlation between two continuous variables.
- o The polychoric correlation is a correlation between two ordinal variables.
- o The polyserial correlation is a correlation between one ordinal variable and one continuous variable.
- o If all variables are ordinal, all correlations will be polychoric correlations.
- o If all variables are continuous, all correlations will be product-moment correlations.
- o In all other cases, all three types of correlations will be present in the PM matrix.

Carefully note these comments about the files that can be saved:

- o SA or AC (save asymptotic covariance matrix) and SV (save asymptotic variances) are available only when MA=CM (Default), MA=AM, MA=KM, or MA=PM and only if TR=LI. However, see page 171 in Appendix B on for estimating the asymptotic covariance matrix when MA=OM, MA=RM, or MA=TM.
  (Examples 6A–6C in Chapter 4 illustrate these options.)
- o SA (or AC) and SV require *large samples*.
  In LISREL, these asymptotic estimates may do more harm than good if they are based on too small samples. See page 171 in Appendix B.

- o The estimated asymptotic variances and covariances will be written to the specified file in binary format. When the utility BIN2ASC is used to convert this into an ASCII file, the file is written as one long vector with the format (6D13.6); *i.e.*, with 6 numbers per line. The length of the vector depends on $p = k(k+1)/2$ and $q = k(k-1)/2$, the value of MA, and whether SA or SV has been requested:

	SA	SV
MA = CM	$[p(p+1)]/2$	p
MA = KM	$[q(q+1)]/2$	q
MA = PM	$[q(q+1)]/2$	q

Computation of the asymptotic variances and covariances is very time consuming and requires a large amount of memory when the number of variables is large. Whether or not it is possible to use these options depends on how much workspace and CPU time are available. The program itself does not have fixed limits on memory or time. See also the section "Workspace" in Chapter 2, page 36.

Bootstrap estimates of the matrix specified with MA=*XX* (*XX*=CM, KM, PM, OM, RM, TM, etc.) on the OU command and its asymptotic covariance matrix specified with SA=*filename* or AC=*filename* may be obtained. This is controlled with these keywords on the OU command: BS, SF, IX, BM, ME, and SD.

If BS=n, the MA-matrix in the output will be the mean of all n bootstrap estimates and the AC-matrix will be the empirical covariance matrix of all n bootstrap estimates. The latter is often a better estimate than that estimated from asymptotic theory. Note that this option makes it possible to estimate the asymptotic covariance matrix for OM, RM, TM matrices that are otherwise not available.

EXAMPLES

Example 1

Suppose $k = 3$ and MA = CM. The CM matrix contains the $p = 6$ elements below the diagonal and in the diagonal, reading rowwise $s' = (s_{11}, s_{21}, s_{22}, s_{31}, s_{32}, s_{33})$.

The vector saved with SV contains the $p = 6$ asymptotic variances of these elements, and the matrix saved with SA is the asymptotic covariance matrix of s. This covariance matrix contains 21 elements in and below the diagonal.

Example 2

Suppose $k = 3$ and MA = KM or PM. The correlation matrix contains the $p = 3$ elements below the diagonal, reading rowwise $r' = (r_{21}, r_{31}, r_{32})$.

The vector saved with SV contains the $q = 3$ asymptotic variances of these correlations, and the matrix saved with SA is the asymptotic covariance matrix of r. This covariance matrix contains 6 elements in and below the diagonal.

Example 3

The file EFFICACY.RAW contains data on six ordinal variables for 297 cases. The following command file will generate 50 bootstrap samples of 148 (50%) cases each and estimate the RM-matrix (Spearman rank correlations) for each of these samples.

All the estimated RM matrices are saved in the file BOOTSTR.RML, their mean is saved in the file EFFICACY.RMB, and 141 times their covariance matrix is saved in the file EFFICACY.ACR, in binary form.

```
EXAMPLE 9
ESTIMATING RM AND AC MATRICES BY BOOTSTRAP
DA NI=6
LA=EFFICACY.LAB
RA=EFFICACY.RAW FO;(6F1.0)
OU MA=RM BS=50 SF=50 RM=EFFICACY.RMB AC=EFFICACY.ACR BM=BOOTSTR.RML
```

Example 4

Suppose, the raw data contains many cases and very many variables written in a complicated format with lots of redundant spaces and digits. The file containing the raw data is very large and it takes a long time to read it each time. Suppose, we wish to save the raw data on a small subset of the variables (and possibly also for a subset of the cases) in a compact form for future use and documentation. This can be done by reading the subset of variables by format or SD commands and saving the new raw data by putting SR=*filename* on the OU command. Instead of SR=*filename*, one can write RA=*filename* and the format of the new data file can be specified by WI=*width-of-format* and ND=*number-of-decimals*.

For example, if the data on the selected variables are single-digit positive numbers, as is often the case, WI=1 ND=0, will save the data in one-column fields. This will save a lot of space and in future PRELIS runs, the data can be read much faster by the format (nF1.0).

The following command file saves the raw data on the six variables after imputation and listwise deletion. The new raw data is saved in the file EFFICACY.RAW in the format (6F1.0).

```
EXAMPLE 7E
Saving the Raw Data after Imputation and Listwise Deletion
DA NI=6 MI=8,9
LA;NOSAY VOTING COMPLEX NOCARE TOUCH INTEREST
RA FI=EX7.RAW FO;(141X,6F2.0)
IM (NOSAY - INTEREST) (NOSAY - INTEREST)
CL NOSAY - INTEREST 1=DS 2=D 3=A 4=AS
OU RA=EFFICACY.RAW WI=1 ND=0
```

The file EFFICACY.RAW has 297 lines of 6 columns and contains the complete data on the six variables for further study.

4 Examples and exercises

This chapter presents a number of examples illustrating the use of PRE-LIS.[1] There are probably thousands of ways the program can be used if we consider all the ways variables can be declared and transformed and all the different types of moment matrices that can be obtained. Only a very small fraction of these can be shown here. The ones we have chosen illustrate the more important procedures PRELIS offers.

These examples are computed from test problems included in the PRE-LIS distribution package. Sections of the output (slightly edited) are presented with explanations and comments given in *italics*.

4.1 Compute matrix of polyserial and polychoric correlations (MA=PM)

Data for Example 1A consist of the first hundred cases of the artificial data described in Chapter 2. Data are stored in a file named DATA.100. We examine the data and use the PM option to compute the matrix of polychoric and polyserial correlations.

There are six variables. Two of them (variables 1 and 5) are continuous, labeled CONTIN1 and CONTIN2. Four others (variables 2, 3, 4, and 6) are ordinal, labeled ORDINAL1, ORDINAL2, ORDINAL3, and ORDINAL4.

The number "−9" is used to represent missing values.

---

[1]Appendix C and D contain some specific PRELIS 2 examples.

```
EXAMPLE 1A: PRELIS TEST ON DATA.100
DA NI = 6   NOBS = 100    MISSING = -9    TREATMENT = PAIRWISE
RAW-DATA = DATA.100
LABELS
CONTIN1 ORDINAL1 ORDINAL2 ORDINAL3 CONTIN2 ORDINAL4
CONTINUOUS: CONTIN1 CONTIN2
OUTPUT MATRIX = PMATRIX
```

PRELIS lists all the commands in the output file, so that their correct interpretation can be confirmed. If a syntax error is found, an error message will appear just below the line where the error is located. The program will stop running this problem and will continue with the next problem, if any.

```
Number of Missing Values per Variable

   CONTIN1   ORDINAL1   ORDINAL2   ORDINAL3   CONTIN2   ORDINAL4
  --------   --------   --------   --------   --------   --------
        21         16         22         25        24         20


Distribution of Missing Values

Total Sample Size =     100

Number of Missing Values   0   1   2   3   4
          Number of Cases  23  40  25  10   2
```

There are 23 cases with no missing values, 40 with one missing value, etc. If listwise deletion had been used, the effective sample size would have been 23. As the data matrix consists of 100 cases, this may seem like a very large reduction in the sample size. But this is actually typical of what will happen if 20 percent (approximately 120 out of 600) of the observations are missing at random.

```
Effective Sample Sizes
Univariate (in Diagonal) and Pairwise Bivariate (off Diagonal)

             CONTIN1   ORDINAL1   ORDINAL2   ORDINAL3   CONTIN2   ORDINAL4
            --------   --------   --------   --------   --------   --------
  CONTIN1         79
 ORDINAL1         64         84
 ORDINAL2         60         63         78
 ORDINAL3         58         65         62         75
  CONTIN2         59         63         58         57        76
 ORDINAL4         65         67         64         60        62         80
```

4 EXAMPLES AND EXERCISES

There are 79 cases with no missing values on CONTIN1; 64 cases with no missing values on both CONTIN1 and ORDINAL1; etc. These are the effective sample sizes that will be used under pairwise deletion.

```
Percentage of Missing Values
Univariate (in Diagonal) and Pairwise Bivariate (off Diagonal)

              CONTIN1   ORDINAL1  ORDINAL2  ORDINAL3  CONTIN2   ORDINAL4
              --------  --------  --------  --------  --------  --------
CONTIN1        21.00
ORDINAL1       36.00     16.00
ORDINAL2       40.00     37.00     22.00
ORDINAL3       42.00     35.00     38.00     25.00
CONTIN2        41.00     37.00     42.00     43.00     24.00
ORDINAL4       35.00     33.00     36.00     40.00     38.00     20.00
```

This table provides basically the same information as the previous table, but in terms of percentage of missing observations. Thus, 21 percent of the 100 cases are missing on CONTIN1; 36 percent are missing on both CONTIN1 and ORDINAL1; etc.

```
Univariate Distributions for Ordinal Variables

ORDINAL1 Frequency Percentage Bar Chart
    1        4        4.8     ****
    2       15       17.9     **************
    3        6        7.1     ******          .
    4        6        7.1     ******
    5       11       13.1     **********
    6       17       20.2     ****************
    7       25       29.8     ************************

ORDINAL2 Frequency Percentage Bar Chart
    1       28       35.9     ***************************
    2       14       17.9     *************
    3        6        7.7     ******
    4        9       11.5     *********
    5       21       26.9     ********************

ORDINAL3 Frequency Percentage Bar Chart
    1       14       18.7     *************
    2       44       58.7     *******************************************
    3       17       22.7     ****************

ORDINAL4 Frequency Percentage Bar Chart
    1       24       30.0     *******************
    2       56       70.0     ******************************************
```

For each ordinal variable, this table shows which score values were found in the data and the categories to which the scores correspond. This table also gives the marginal frequency distribution, in terms of absolute and relative frequences and a bar chart. In this case, it is seen that ORDINAL1 has a skewed distribution, and ORDINAL2 has a U-shaped distribution.

```
Bivariate Distributions for Ordinal Variables (Frequencies)
```

	ORDINAL2					ORDINAL3			ORDINAL4	
ORDINAL1	1	2	3	4	5	1	2	3	1	2
1	2	0	1	0	0	1	1	0	2	1
2	6	1	0	0	2	3	9	1	8	3
3	3	1	0	1	1	0	2	1	3	3
4	2	2	0	0	1	3	2	1	0	2
5	2	4	0	1	1	2	5	1	2	7
6	5	0	2	3	4	2	8	3	2	11
7	4	3	2	1	8	0	12	8	5	18

	ORDINAL3			ORDINAL4	
ORDINAL2	1	2	3	1	2
1	8	10	2	7	15
2	4	6	3	4	9
3	0	4	2	3	1
4	0	4	2	0	6
5	0	9	8	2	17

	ORDINAL4	
ORDINAL3	1	2
1	4	7
2	11	24
3	3	11

This is a compact way of presenting contingency tables for all pairs of ordinal variables. Each contingency table is based on all cases with real observations of both variables. The sample sizes for each contingency table are those given by the off diagonal elements in the table "Effective Sample Sizes" (described earlier).

```
Univariate Summary Statistics for Continuous Variables
```

Variable	Mean	St. Dev.	T-Value	Skewness	Kurtosis	Minimum	Freq.	Maximum	Freq.
CONTIN1	-0.011	1.189	-0.083	-0.040	-0.644	-2.200	1	2.930	1
CONTIN2	-0.164	1.082	-1.320	-0.215	-0.021	-3.260	1	2.450	1

This table gives useful information about the marginal distribution of each continuous variable. The measures of skewness and kurtosis are γ_1 and γ_2 (see Kendall & Stuart, 1963, pp. 85–86), which are both zero for a normal distribution. To enable checking for clustering of observations at either end, the table also gives minimum and maximum values and their respective frequencies.

```
Bivariate Summary Statistics for Pairs of Variables
(The First Variable is Ordinal and the Second is Continuous)

ORDINAL1 vs.  CONTIN1
--------      --------
Category  Number of Observations  Mean  Standard Deviation
--------  ----------------------  ----  ------------------
    1                4            -1.468       0.224
    2               11            -1.165       0.928
    3                4            -0.162       0.489
    4                4             0.400       0.780
    5                7             0.336       0.569
    6               13             0.391       0.812
    7               21             0.796       0.893

ORDINAL2 vs.  CONTIN1
--------      --------
Category  Number of Observations  Mean  Standard Deviation
--------  ----------------------  ----  ------------------
    1               21            -0.499       1.109
    2               12            -0.102       1.207
    3                5             0.058       1.297
    4                7             0.146       0.731
    5               15             0.571       1.361

ORDINAL3 vs.  CONTIN1
--------      --------
Category  Number of Observations  Mean  Standard Deviation
--------  ----------------------  ----  ------------------
    1               13            -0.435       1.229
    2               35             0.003       1.165
    3               10             0.784       1.182

ORDINAL1 vs.  CONTIN2
--------      --------
Category  Number of Observations  Mean  Standard Deviation
--------  ----------------------  ----  ------------------
    1                3            -0.793       1.299
    2               11            -0.200       0.747
    3                4            -0.050       1.217
    4                4            -0.235       1.089
    5                8            -0.224       1.138
    6               13            -0.235       0.804
    7               20             0.233       1.055
```

```
ORDINAL2 vs.  CONTIN2
--------     --------
Category  Number of Observations  Mean  Standard Deviation
--------  ----------------------  ----  ------------------
   1                22            -0.655        0.919
   2                 9             0.166        1.394
   3                 4             0.235        0.391
   4                 7            -0.234        1.211
   5                16             0.096        0.934

ORDINAL3 vs.  CONTIN2
--------     --------
Category  Number of Observations  Mean  Standard Deviation
--------  ----------------------  ----  ------------------
   1                 7            -1.133        1.603
   2                35             0.088        1.010
   3                15             0.025        0.655

ORDINAL4 vs.  CONTIN1
--------     --------
Category  Number of Observations  Mean  Standard Deviation
--------  ----------------------  ----  ------------------
   1                20            -0.356        1.414
   2                45             0.184        1.113

ORDINAL4 vs.  CONTIN2
--------     --------
Category  Number of Observations  Mean  Standard Deviation
--------  ----------------------  ----  ------------------
   1                20            -0.155        1.260
   2                42            -0.078        0.903
```

These tables give summary statistics for each pair of variables: one is ordinal, one is continuous. The table gives the mean and standard deviation of the continuous variable for each category of the ordinal variable. The overall mean of the continuous variable was subtracted from all the values before these summary statistics were computed.

```
                      Correlations and Test Statistics

           (PE=Pearson Product Moment, PC=Polychoric, PS=Polyserial)
                                     Test of Model     Test of Close Fit
   Variable vs. Variable Correlation Chi-Squ. D.F. P-Value  RMSEA P-Value
   -------- --- -------- ----------- -------- ---- -------  ----- -------
   ORDINAL1 vs.  CONTIN1  0.706 (PS)  21.456   11  0.029   0.122  0.069
   ORDINAL2 vs.  CONTIN1  0.382 (PS)   3.464    7  0.839   0.000  0.886
   ORDINAL2 vs. ORDINAL1  0.389 (PC)  23.831   23  0.413   0.024  0.608
   ORDINAL3 vs.  CONTIN1  0.349 (PS)   0.333    3  0.954   0.000  0.962
   ORDINAL3 vs. ORDINAL1  0.438 (PC)   8.745   11  0.645   0.000  0.758
```

```
ORDINAL3 vs. ORDINAL2  0.562 (PC)   6.187    7  0.518  0.000  0.619
CONTIN2  vs.  CONTIN1   0.208 (PE)
ORDINAL1 vs.  CONTIN2   0.243 (PS)   4.403   11  0.957  0.000  0.976
ORDINAL2 vs.  CONTIN2   0.304 (PS)  10.668    7  0.154  0.095  0.230
ORDINAL3 vs.  CONTIN2   0.275 (PS)  12.588    3  0.006  0.237  0.011
ORDINAL4 vs.  CONTIN1   0.258 (PS)   1.587    1  0.208  0.095  0.244
ORDINAL4 vs. ORDINAL1   0.473 (PC)   6.369    5  0.272  0.064  0.364
ORDINAL4 vs. ORDINAL2   0.310 (PC)   8.365    3  0.039  0.167  0.064
ORDINAL4 vs. ORDINAL3   0.160 (PC)   0.061    1  0.804  0.000  0.818
ORDINAL4 vs.  CONTIN2   0.044 (PS)   2.941    1  0.086  0.177  0.111
```

For each pair of variables for which a polychoric or polyserial correlation has been estimated, this table provides a goodness-of-fit test of the model of an underlying bivariate normal distribution. Such a test is not provided when the estimated correlation is a product moment correlation. The table also gives statistics for testing the hypothesis that the correlation in the bivariate normal distribution is zero.

```
Correlation Matrix

           CONTIN1   ORDINAL1  ORDINAL2  ORDINAL3  CONTIN2   ORDINAL4
           --------  --------  --------  --------  --------  --------
CONTIN1     1.000
ORDINAL1    0.706     1.000
ORDINAL2    0.382     0.389     1.000
ORDINAL3    0.349     0.438     0.562     1.000
CONTIN2     0.208     0.243     0.304     0.275     1.000
ORDINAL4    0.258     0.473     0.310     0.160     0.044     1.000
```

This correlation matrix may be saved in a file by specifying SM = filename on the OU command.

Computer exercise 1

Run the same data using the KM and OM specifications.

Compare the correlations.

4.2   Logarithmic transformations and recoding of variables

As a variation of the previous example, in Example 1B we transform CON-TIN1 by a logarithmic transformation

$$y = \log(3 + x)$$

and dichotomize ORDINAL1 and ORDINAL2 as evenly as possible. For the transformed data, we compute the matrix of product moment correlations using normal scores for the ordinal variables. This time we use listwise deletion.

```
EXAMPLE 1B: PRELIS TEST ON DATA.100
DA NI = 6   NOBS = 100   MISSING = -9   TREATMENT = LISTWISE
RAW-DATA-FROM FILE = DATA.100
LABELS
CONTIN1 ORDINAL1 ORDINAL2 ORDINAL3 CONTIN2 ORDINAL4
CONTINUOUS: CONTIN1 CONTIN2
LO CONTIN1 AL= 3
RECODE   ORDINAL1   OLD=1-5,6-7   NEW=0,1
RECODE   ORDINAL2   OLD=1-2,3-5   NEW=0,1
NSCORES ORDINAL1 - ORDINAL3 ORDINAL4
OUTPUT   MATRIX = KM
```

The log transformation of CONTIN1 is safe because we found in the previous run that the smallest observed value on CONTIN1 was -2.2. Note that only two recode commands are needed in this case to di-choto-mize ORDINAL1 and ORDINAL2.

```
Distribution of Missing Values

Total Sample Size =     100

Number of Missing Values    0   1   2   3   4
        Number of Cases    23  40  25  10   2
Listwise Deletion

Total Effective Sample Size =     23
```

Of the 100 cases, there are only 23 with complete data on all variables. Since TR=LI has been specified, 23 will be the sample size in this run.

Univariate Summary Statistics for Continuous Variables

Variable	Mean	St. Dev.	T-Value	Skewness	Kurtosis	Minimum	Freq.	Maximum	Freq.
CONTIN1	1.012	0.464	10.461	-0.890	-0.303	-0.062	1	1.651	1
ORDINAL1	0.000	0.793	0.000	-0.684	-1.735	-1.062	8	0.567	15
ORDINAL2	0.000	0.815	0.000	-0.093	-2.179	-0.833	11	0.764	12
ORDINAL3	0.000	0.887	0.000	-0.039	-0.093	-1.626	3	1.353	5
CONTIN2	-0.118	0.884	-0.639	-0.161	-0.633	-1.960	1	1.510	1
ORDINAL4	0.000	0.757	0.000	-1.167	-0.874	-1.246	6	0.440	17

The values of CONTIN1 have been transformed to a logarithmic scale. OR-DINAL1 and ORDINAL2 have first been dichotomized to have scores 0 and 1. These scores have then been converted to normal scores. The mean of the normal scores is zero

Correlation Matrix

	CONTIN1	ORDINAL1	ORDINAL2	ORDINAL3	CONTIN2	ORDINAL4
CONTIN1	1.000					
ORDINAL1	0.461	1.000				
ORDINAL2	0.139	0.215	1.000			
ORDINAL3	0.137	0.421	0.442	1.000		
CONTIN2	0.061	-0.205	0.394	0.121	1.000	
ORDINAL4	0.407	0.606	0.224	0.089	-0.286	1.000

4.3 Select cases, estimate augmented moment matrix (MA=AM)

As a second variation of the first example, in Example 1C we use the original 100 observations and select those cases which have values larger than zero on CONTIN1. For these cases, we estimate the augmented moment matrix.

```
EXAMPLE 1C: PRELIS TEST ON DATA.100
DA NI=6 NO=100 MI=-9 TR=PA;RA=DATA.100;LA
CONTIN1 ORDINAL1 ORDINAL2 ORDINAL3 CONTIN2 ORDINAL4
CONTINUOUS: CONTIN1 CONTIN2;SC CONTIN1 >0;OU MA=AM SR=SELDATA
```

As shown here, several PRELIS commands can be on the same physical line. Raw data for the selected subsample will be saved in the file SELDATA.

```
Distribution of Missing Values

Total Sample Size =      44

Number of Missing Values    0   1   2   3   4
          Number of Cases  13  18  11   1   1
```

The total selected subsample is 44, but it includes cases with missing values. In this run, pairwise deletion is used in the selected subsample.

```
Effective Sample Sizes
Univariate (in Diagonal) and Pairwise Bivariate (off Diagonal)

              CONTIN1   ORDINAL1   ORDINAL2   ORDINAL3   CONTIN2   ORDINAL4
              --------  --------   --------   --------   --------  --------
  CONTIN1        44
  ORDINAL1       39        39
  ORDINAL2       34        29        34
  ORDINAL3       33        30        29        33
  CONTIN2        30        27        21        22        30
  ORDINAL4       37        32        29        27        26        37
    CONST.       44        39        34        33        30        37

              CONST.
              --------
    CONST.       44
```

```
Percentage of Missing Values
Univariate (in Diagonal) and Pairwise Bivariate (off Diagonal)

              CONTIN1   ORDINAL1   ORDINAL2   ORDINAL3   CONTIN2   ORDINAL4
              --------  --------   --------   --------   --------  --------
  CONTIN1       0.00
  ORDINAL1      11.36     11.36
  ORDINAL2      22.73     34.09     22.73
  ORDINAL3      25.00     31.82     34.09     25.00
  CONTIN2       31.82     38.64     52.27     50.00     31.82
  ORDINAL4      15.91     27.27     34.09     38.64     40.91     15.91
    CONST.       0.00     11.36     22.73     25.00     31.82     15.91

              CONST.
              --------
    CONST.      0.00
```

Since the augmented moment matrix was requested, i.e., MA=AM, the program automatically adds the variable CONST. which has the value 1 for each case.

Univariate Summary Statistics for Continuous Variables

Variable	Mean	St. Dev.	T-Value	Skewness	Kurtosis	Minimum	Freq.	Maximum	Freq.
CONTIN1	0.858	0.667	8.533	1.143	0.775	0.020	1	2.930	1
ORDINAL1	5.846	1.329	27.479	-1.193	0.653	2.000	1	7.000	16
ORDINAL2	3.029	1.696	10.413	-0.009	-1.796	1.000	10	5.000	11
ORDINAL3	2.000	0.661	17.370	0.000	-0.675	1.000	7	3.000	7
CONTIN2	0.123	1.041	0.645	-0.250	-0.835	-1.960	1	1.720	1
ORDINAL4	1.784	0.417	25.999	-1.438	-0.096	1.000	8	2.000	29

These are summary statistics for the subsample of cases with positive values of CONTIN1.

Augmented Moment Matrix

	CONTIN1	ORDINAL1	ORDINAL2	ORDINAL3	CONTIN2	ORDINAL4
CONTIN1	1.171					
ORDINAL1	5.374	35.897				
ORDINAL2	3.003	18.520	11.971			
ORDINAL3	1.872	11.900	6.635	4.424		
CONTIN2	0.097	0.940	0.934	0.311	1.063	
ORDINAL4	1.492	10.451	5.512	3.568	0.139	3.351
CONST.	0.858	5.846	3.029	2.000	0.123	1.784

Augmented Moment Matrix

	CONST.
CONST.	1.000

The last row of the augmented moment matrix contains means of variables in the selected subsample.

Because the program assumes an 80 column output format by default, this matrix is printed in sections. If you have a printer that can print 132 characters per line, you can request WP (for wide print) on the OU command and the matrix will be printed in one section.

4.4 Polychoric correlation matrix with all variables ordinal (MA=PM)

Swedish school children in grade 9 were asked questions about their attitudes on social issues in family, school, and society. Among the questions asked were the following eight items [in free translation from Swedish] (Hasselrot & Lernberg, 1980).

For me, questions about . . .

1. human rights

2. equal conditions for all people

3. racial problems

4. equal value of all people

5. euthanasia

6. crime and punishment

7. conscientious objectors

8. guilt and bad conscience

are:

___ unimportant   ___ not important   ___ important   ___ very important

For Example 2, we use a subsample of 200 cases. Responses to the eight questions were scored 1, 2, 3, and 4 (4 = very important). Missing values were scored zero. The data matrix consists of 200 rows and 8 columns. It is stored in the file DATA.EX2.

```
EXAMPLE 2: ATTITUDES OF MORALITY AND EQUALITY
DA NI=8 MI=0 TR=PA
LA
HUMRGHTS EQUALCON RACEPROB EQUALVAL EUTHANAS CRIMEPUN CONSCOBJ GUILT
RA=DATA.EX2
OU MA=PM

Number of Missing Values per Variable

 HUMRGHTS  EQUALCON  RACEPROB  EQUALVAL  EUTHANAS  CRIMEPUN  CONSCOBJ  GUILT
 --------  --------  --------  --------  --------  --------  --------  --------
        2         1         3         0         0         0         0         1

Distribution of Missing Values

Total Sample Size =    200

Number of Missing Values    0    1    2    3
        Number of Cases   195    4    0    1
```

There are only five cases with missing values!

(Three sections of the output have been skipped at this point.)

```
Bivariate Distributions for Ordinal Variables (Frequencies)

             EQUALCON            RACEPROB            EQUALVAL
          ------------------   ------------------   ------------------
HUMRGHTS   1    2    3    4     1    2    3    4     1    2    3    4
          ------------------   ------------------   ------------------
     1     0    0    2    1     2    0    0    1     0    0    2    1
     2     3    4    4    1     0    2    7    3     3    6    3    0
     3     0   13   39   21     6    7   36   24     2   24   28   19
     4     2    7   41   60     7    8   41   52     5   16   34   55

             EUTHANAS            CRIMEPUN            CONSCOBJ
          ------------------   ------------------   ------------------
HUMRGHTS   1    2    3    4     1    2    3    4     1    2    3    4
          ------------------   ------------------   ------------------
     1     0    0    2    1     0    0    1    2     0    1    1    1
     2     3    4    4    1     0    5    6    1     6    4    1    1
     3     2    9   40   22     0   11   41   21    13   22   31    7
     4     2    9   31   68     2   10   50   48    20   24   43   23
```

Only a few of the contingency tables are given here. These show, for example, that of the 110 students who think that human rights are very important, 60 think that equal conditions are also very important.

```
                      Correlations and Test Statistics

          (PE=Pearson Product Moment, PC=Polychoric, PS=Polyserial)
                                      Test of Model      Test of Close Fit
Variable vs. Variable Correlation  Chi-Squ. D.F. P-Value   RMSEA P-Value
-------- --- -------- -----------  -------- ---- -------   ----- -------
EQUALCON vs. HUMRGHTS  0.418 (PC)   14.708    8   0.065    0.065  0.274
RACEPROB vs. HUMRGHTS  0.221 (PC)   10.872    8   0.209    0.043  0.516
RACEPROB vs. EQUALCON  0.202 (PC)    4.933    8   0.765    0.000  0.925
EQUALVAL vs. HUMRGHTS  0.373 (PC)   16.735    8   0.033    0.074  0.184
EQUALVAL vs. EQUALCON  0.635 (PC)   13.097    8   0.109    0.057  0.367
EQUALVAL vs. RACEPROB  0.285 (PC)   10.408    8   0.238    0.039  0.552
EUTHANAS vs. HUMRGHTS  0.442 (PC)   12.341    8   0.137    0.052  0.415
EUTHANAS vs. EQUALCON  0.706 (PC)    9.872    8   0.274    0.034  0.596
EUTHANAS vs. RACEPROB  0.317 (PC)    7.348    8   0.500    0.000  0.783
EUTHANAS vs. EQUALVAL  0.692 (PC)   26.238    8   0.001    0.107  0.019
CRIMEPUN vs. HUMRGHTS  0.215 (PC)   12.460    8   0.132    0.053  0.407
CRIMEPUN vs. EQUALCON  0.236 (PC)   17.785    8   0.023    0.078  0.148
CRIMEPUN vs. RACEPROB  0.282 (PC)   14.366    8   0.073    0.064  0.291
CRIMEPUN vs. EQUALVAL  0.423 (PC)   13.672    8   0.091    0.060  0.334
CRIMEPUN vs. EUTHANAS  0.218 (PC)   13.103    8   0.108    0.056  0.368
```

```
CONSCOBJ vs. HUMRGHTS  0.190 (PC)  11.504  8  0.175  0.047  0.473
CONSCOBJ vs. EQUALCON  0.292 (PC)  10.694  8  0.220  0.041  0.533
CONSCOBJ vs. RACEPROB  0.312 (PC)   6.467  8  0.595  0.000  0.842
CONSCOBJ vs. EQUALVAL  0.340 (PC)  14.912  8  0.061  0.066  0.266
CONSCOBJ vs. EUTHANAS  0.224 (PC)   7.263  8  0.509  0.000  0.792
CONSCOBJ vs. CRIMEPUN  0.312 (PC)   9.113  8  0.333  0.026  0.655
   GUILT vs. HUMRGHTS  0.094 (PC)  17.361  8  0.027  0.077  0.160
   GUILT vs. EQUALCON  0.314 (PC)  15.453  8  0.051  0.069  0.238
   GUILT vs. RACEPROB  0.239 (PC)   8.626  8  0.375  0.020  0.688
   GUILT vs. EQUALVAL  0.320 (PC)   7.392  8  0.495  0.000  0.782
   GUILT vs. EUTHANAS  0.340 (PC)   8.500  8  0.386  0.018  0.701
   GUILT vs. CRIMEPUN  0.207 (PC)   7.595  8  0.474  0.000  0.768
   GUILT vs. CONSCOBJ  0.202 (PC)  12.879  8  0.116  0.055  0.381

     Percentage of Tests Exceeding 0.5% Significance Level:  0.0%

     Percentage of Tests Exceeding 1.0% Significance Level:  0.0%

     Percentage of Tests Exceeding 5.0% Significance Level:  3.6%
```

Despite the fact that most of the marginal distributions are highly skewed, only 1 out of 28 of the model tests reject the hypothesis of an underlying bivariate normal distribution at the 1 percent nominal level of significance. When examining many tests like this, bear in mind that if all the hypotheses were true, a 1 percent long-run rejectance rate should be expected by pure chance.

```
Correlation Matrix

          HUMRGHTS  EQUALCON  RACEPROB  EQUALVAL  EUTHANAS  CRIMEPUN
          --------  --------  --------  --------  --------  --------
HUMRGHTS     1.000
EQUALCON     0.418     1.000
RACEPROB     0.221     0.202     1.000
EQUALVAL     0.373     0.635     0.285     1.000
EUTHANAS     0.442     0.706     0.317     0.692     1.000
CRIMEPUN     0.215     0.236     0.282     0.423     0.218     1.000
CONSCOBJ     0.190     0.292     0.312     0.340     0.224     0.312
   GUILT     0.094     0.314     0.239     0.320     0.340     0.207

Correlation Matrix

          CONSCOBJ     GUILT
          --------  --------
CONSCOBJ     1.000
   GUILT     0.202     1.000
```

Computer exercise 2

Run the same data using the RM or OM specifications.

Compare the correlations.

4.5 Censored variables

The data in the file DATA.EX3 consist of scores of Swedish school children on reading and spelling tests that relate to metaphonological aspects of the Swedish language. Each score is the number of correctly answered items. There are 11 tests and 90 cases. In the first run (Example 3A), we treat all variables as continuous and estimate the product-moment correlations. In the second run (Example 3B), after observing that some of the tests have large "floor" and "ceiling" effects, we declare all variables as censored and reestimate the product-moment correlations.

```
EXAMPLE 3A: TEST SCORE DATA
DA NI=11 NO=90
LA=LABELS.EX3
RA=DATA.EX3
CO ALL
OU MA=KM
```

In Example 3A, all variables are continuous. The labels are read from a file called LABELS.EX3.

Univariate Summary Statistics for Continuous Variables

Variable	Mean	St. Dev.	T-Value	Skewness	Kurtosis	Minimum	Freq.	Maximum	Freq.
V01	21.789	7.856	26.312	-1.117	0.256	0.000	2	30.000	6
V02	14.622	7.048	19.682	-0.173	-0.616	0.000	2	28.000	5
V07	11.489	3.069	35.510	-0.175	2.520	0.000	1	20.000	2
V08	14.478	3.660	37.523	-0.490	2.785	0.000	1	25.000	1
V09	19.122	6.830	26.561	-0.635	0.282	0.000	3	32.000	1
V10	21.622	5.560	36.894	-0.553	0.092	6.000	1	33.000	2
V21	15.022	2.998	47.535	-1.956	3.247	4.000	1	17.000	41
V22	13.122	3.304	37.676	-1.123	0.838	2.000	1	17.000	8
V23	12.578	3.402	35.076	-1.141	0.645	3.000	3	16.000	21
V24	8.611	3.550	23.014	-0.271	-0.599	0.000	1	15.000	2
V25	16.589	4.271	36.844	-1.338	2.280	1.000	1	22.000	9

V21 has a high negative skewness; V07, V08, V21, and V25 have high kurtoses; and V21 and V23 have high ceiling effects. Obviously, V21 is a very problematic variable. For data like these, it is likely that the correlations will be biased due to restrictions of range.

Correlation Matrix

	V01	V02	V07	V08	V09	V10
V01	1.000					
V02	0.755	1.000				
V07	0.634	0.599	1.000			
V08	0.640	0.618	0.872	1.000		
V09	0.474	0.429	0.345	0.377	1.000	
V10	0.309	0.423	0.339	0.330	0.581	1.000
V21	0.554	0.568	0.393	0.423	0.296	0.322
V22	0.509	0.527	0.434	0.399	0.309	0.360
V23	0.518	0.596	0.484	0.474	0.425	0.489
V24	0.662	0.672	0.603	0.569	0.503	0.529
V25	0.726	0.756	0.528	0.516	0.380	0.397

Correlation Matrix

	V21	V22	V23	V24	V25
V21	1.000				
V22	0.625	1.000			
V23	0.564	0.519	1.000		
V24	0.538	0.613	0.558	1.000	
V25	0.731	0.634	0.619	0.628	1.000

In the second run, Example 3B, we treat all variables as censored below and above.

```
EXAMPLE 3B: TEST SCORE DATA
DA NI=11 NO=90
LA=LABELS.EX3
RA=DATA.EX3
CE ALL
OU MA=KM
```

Output from the second run follows on the next page.

4 EXAMPLES AND EXERCISES

Univariate Summary Statistics for Continuous Variables

Variable	Mean	St. Dev.	T-Value	Skewness	Kurtosis	Minimum	Freq.	Maximum	Freq.
V01	22.031	8.411	24.849	-0.987	0.477	-2.628	2	34.506	6
V02	14.727	7.536	18.539	-0.032	-0.119	-2.853	2	31.032	5
V07	11.502	3.165	34.471	-0.119	3.131	-0.772	1	20.972	2
V08	14.480	3.737	36.762	-0.500	3.366	-0.865	1	26.109	1
V09	19.081	7.108	25.467	-0.748	0.908	-2.182	3	34.808	1
V10	21.651	5.723	35.888	-0.487	0.456	4.266	1	35.147	2
V21	16.444	4.191	37.219	-1.059	0.639	2.804	1	20.150	41
V22	13.275	3.569	35.287	-0.861	0.861	1.028	1	18.844	8
V23	13.116	4.216	29.510	-0.656	0.265	1.600	3	18.506	21
V24	8.630	3.650	22.428	-0.233	-0.321	-1.224	1	16.476	2
V25	16.810	4.665	34.187	-0.966	1.976	-0.203	1	24.349	9

Both skewness and kurtosis are now smaller than before for all variables, and the maximum and minimum values have been moved further out.

Correlation Matrix

	V01	V02	V07	V08	V09	V10
V01	1.000					
V02	0.759	1.000				
V07	0.649	0.605	1.000			
V08	0.637	0.610	0.873	1.000		
V09	0.484	0.421	0.355	0.373	1.000	
V10	0.315	0.431	0.344	0.320	0.563	1.000
V21	0.558	0.579	0.446	0.464	0.345	0.336
V22	0.515	0.545	0.431	0.399	0.300	0.361
V23	0.505	0.584	0.487	0.457	0.438	0.483
V24	0.674	0.693	0.613	0.570	0.497	0.535
V25	0.715	0.768	0.541	0.515	0.387	0.417

Correlation Matrix

	V21	V22	V23	V24	V25
V21	1.000				
V22	0.590	1.000			
V23	0.536	0.487	1.000		
V24	0.532	0.632	0.552	1.000	
V25	0.692	0.637	0.615	0.644	1.000

Many correlations in this table are smaller than in the previous run, especially those for variables V21 and V23.

4.6 Estimated regressions

Finn (1974) presents the data shown in Table 4.1. These data represent the scores of fifteen freshmen at a large Midwestern university in the United States, on five educational measures:

y_1 = grade average in required courses
y_2 = grade average in elective courses
x_1 = score on general knowledge test taken year before
x_2 = score on IQ test from year before
x_3 = score on educational motivation test from year before

In Example 4, PRELIS estimates the regressions of y_1 and y_2 on x_1, x_2, and x_3.

Complete output for Example 4 follows.

```
EXAMPLE 4: PREDICTION OF GRADE AVERAGES
DA NI=5 NO=15
LA
GRAVEREQ GRAVELEC KNOWLEDG IQPREVYR 'ED MOTIV'
RA=DATA.EX4;CO ALL;RG 1 2 ON 3 4 5;OU MA=CM
```

The commands on the line above illustrate how compact input for this problem can be.

```
Estimated Equations

GRAVEREQ = 0.0854*KNOWLEDG + 0.00822*IQPREVYR - 0.0149*ED MOTIV
           (0.0270)           (0.0485)            (0.112)
            3.168              0.169              -0.134

         + Error, R² = 0.568

Error Variance = 0.257

GRAVELEC = 0.0472*KNOWLEDG + 0.145*IQPREVYR + 0.126*ED MOTIV
           (0.0259)          (0.0467)          (0.107)
            1.823             3.117             1.170

         + Error, R² = 0.685

Error Variance = 0.237

Total Sample Size =    15
```

Table 4.1
Scores for fifteen college freshmen on five educational measures

Observation	y_1	y_2	x_1	x_2	x_3
1	.8	2.0	72	114	17.3
2	2.2	2.2	78	117	17.6
3	1.6	2.0	84	117	15.0
4	2.6	3.7	95	120	18.0
5	2.7	3.2	88	117	18.7
6	2.1	3.2	83	123	17.9
7	3.1	3.7	92	118	17.3
8	3.0	3.1	86	114	18.1
9	3.2	2.6	88	114	16.0
10	2.6	3.2	80	115	16.4
11	2.7	2.8	87	114	17.6
12	3.0	2.4	94	112	19.5
13	1.6	1.4	73	115	12.7
14	.9	1.0	80	111	17.0
15	1.9	1.2	83	112	16.1

Univariate Summary Statistics for Continuous Variables

Variable	Mean	St. Dev.	T-Value	Skewness	Kurtosis	Minimum	Freq.	Maximum	Freq.
GRAVEREQ	2.267	0.771	11.392	-0.709	-0.799	0.800	1	3.200	1
GRAVELEC	2.513	0.868	11.209	-0.362	-1.147	1.000	1	3.700	2
KNOWLEDG	84.200	6.889	47.338	-0.201	-0.787	72.000	1	95.000	1
IQPREVYR	115.533	3.204	139.649	0.836	0.225	111.000	1	123.000	1
ED MOTIV	17.013	1.641	40.145	-1.246	1.687	12.700	1	19.500	1

Covariance Matrix

	GRAVEREQ	GRAVELEC	KNOWLEDG	IQPREVYR	ED MOTIV
GRAVEREQ	0.594				
GRAVELEC	0.483	0.754			
KNOWLEDG	3.993	3.626	47.457		
IQPREVYR	0.426	1.757	4.100	10.267	
ED MOTIV	0.499	0.716	6.261	0.557	2.694

The t-values reveal immediately that only x_1 is a significant predictor of y_1, and only x_2 is a significant predictor of y_2. The variable x_3 is not significant for either purpose. It should be noted, however, that the sample size is too small to draw any safe conclusions.

4.7 Tetrachoric correlations, with asymptotic variances estimated from grouped data

Bock & Lieberman (1970) and Christoffersson (1975) published the data in Table 4.2 giving observed frequencies for the 32 response patterns arising from five items (11 through 15) of Section 6 of the Law School Admissions Test (LSAT). All items are dichotomous.

The sample is a subsample of 1000 from a larger sample of those who took the test. In Example 5, we use this data to illustrate how fast PRELIS can compute tetrachoric correlations for these five items and asymptotic variances of these correlations. Some sections of the output follow.

```
EXAMPLE 5A: LSAT SECTION 6
This example computes the full asymptotic covariance matrix of
tetrachoric correlations which can be used with WLS in LISREL .
See pp. 249-249 of Joreskog and Sorbom (1996): "LISREL 8: User's
Reference Guide." Chicago: Scientific Software International.
```

Table 4.2
Observed frequencies of response patterns for five items of LSAT6

	Response pattern					
Index	1	2	3	4	5	Frequency
1	0	0	0	0	0	3
2	0	0	0	0	1	6
3	0	0	0	1	0	2
4	0	0	0	1	1	11
5	0	0	1	0	0	1
6	0	0	1	0	1	1
7	0	0	1	1	0	3
8	0	0	1	1	1	4
9	0	1	0	0	0	1
10	0	1	0	0	1	8
11	0	1	0	1	0	0
12	0	1	0	1	1	16
13	0	1	1	0	0	0
14	0	1	1	0	1	3
15	0	1	1	1	0	2
16	0	1	1	1	1	15
17	1	0	0	0	0	10
18	1	0	0	0	1	29
19	1	0	0	1	0	14
20	1	0	0	1	1	81
21	1	0	1	0	0	3
22	1	0	1	0	1	28
23	1	0	1	1	0	15
24	1	0	1	1	1	80
25	1	1	0	0	0	16
26	1	1	0	0	1	56
27	1	1	0	1	0	21
28	1	1	0	1	1	173
29	1	1	1	0	0	11
30	1	1	1	0	1	61
31	1	1	1	1	0	28
32	1	1	1	1	1	298
			Total			1000

```
DA NI=6 NO=1000
RA=LSAT6.DAT
WE 6
OU MA=PM AC=LSAT6.ACC PA
```

Total Sample Size =   1000

Thresholds for Ordinal Variables

        VAR 1   -1.433
        VAR 2   -0.550
        VAR 3   -0.133
        VAR 4   -0.716
        VAR 5   -1.126

Univariate Distributions for Ordinal Variables

    VAR 1 Frequency Percentage Bar Chart
        0   76   7.6   ****
        1   924   92.4   **

    VAR 2 Frequency Percentage Bar Chart
        0   291   29.1   ******************
        1   709   70.9   **

    VAR 3 Frequency Percentage Bar Chart
        0   447   44.7   ************************************
        1   553   55.3   **

    VAR 4 Frequency Percentage Bar Chart
        0   237   23.7   ***************
        1   763   76.3   **

    VAR 5 Frequency Percentage Bar Chart
        0   130   13.0   *******
        1   870   87.0   **

Bivariate Distributions for Ordinal Variables (Frequencies)

              VAR 2   VAR 3   VAR 4   VAR 5
            --------   --------   --------   --------
    VAR 1   0   1   0   1   0   1   0   1
            --------   --------   --------   --------
    0   31   45   47   29   23   53   12   64
    1   260   664   400   524   214   710   118   806

              VAR 3   VAR 4   VAR 5
            --------   --------   --------
    VAR 2   0   1   0   1   0   1
            --------   --------   --------
    0   156   135   81   210   51   240
    1   291   418   156   553   79   630

*   *4 EXAMPLES AND EXERCISES*

```
            VAR 4        VAR 5
          --------     --------
VAR 3      0    1       0    1
          --------     --------
0         129  318      67  380
1         108  445      63  490

            VAR 5
          --------
VAR 4      0    1
          --------
0          45  192
1          85  678
```

The joint occurrence proportions (proportions of examinees who give correct answers to both items) for each pair of variables can easily be extracted from these tables.

```
Correlation Matrix

            VAR 1      VAR 2      VAR 3      VAR 4      VAR 5
          --------   --------   --------   --------   --------
VAR 1      1.000
VAR 2      0.170      1.000
VAR 3      0.228      0.189      1.000
VAR 4      0.107      0.111      0.187      1.000
VAR 5      0.067      0.172      0.105      0.201      1.000
```

These correlations essentially agree with those reported by Christoffersson (1975). The largest difference is two units in the third decimal.

```
Asymptotic Covariance Matrix of Correlations

          R(2,1)     R(3,1)     R(3,2)     R(4,1)     R(4,2)     R(4,3)
         --------   --------   --------   --------   --------   --------
R(2,1)    0.00550
R(3,1)    0.00081    0.00505
R(3,2)    0.00039    0.00020    0.00263
R(4,1)    0.00053    0.00118    0.00008    0.00612
R(4,2)    0.00020    0.00006    0.00025    0.00038    0.00322
R(4,3)    0.00004    0.00008    0.00014    0.00056    0.00025    0.00284
R(5,1)    0.00187   -0.00058   -0.00002    0.00076    0.00024    0.00011
R(5,2)    0.00021   -0.00009    0.00012    0.00018    0.00028    0.00012
R(5,3)    0.00003    0.00014    0.00026    0.00016    0.00017    0.00030
R(5,4)    0.00012    0.00012    0.00015    0.00011    0.00021    0.00030
```

```
Asymptotic Covariance Matrix of Correlations

              R(5,1)      R(5,2)      R(5,3)      R(5,4)
            --------    --------    --------    --------
   R(5,1)    0.00819
   R(5,2)    0.00117     0.00409
   R(5,3)    0.00005     0.00036     0.00392
   R(5,4)    0.00027    -0.00002     0.00082     0.00426
```

These are large sample estimates of the variances and covariances of the estimated tetrachoric correlations. The square roots of the variances are the standard errors of the estimated correlations. These can be used to set up approximate confidence intervals for the correlations. For example, an approximate 95 percent confidence interval for ρ_{21} is $.170 \pm 2\sqrt{.00550} = .170 \pm .148$.

4.8   Estimating asymptotic variances and covariances, MA=CM

Examples 6A, 6B, and 6C illustrate how to obtain estimates of asymptotic variances and covariances of the estimated variances, covariances, or correlations between the variables. They are based on generated data consisting of 200 cases on five variables, where the first two variables are continuous and the last three are ordinal. Variables 3, 4, and 5 have 2, 3, and 4 categories, respectively. The data were generated from a population in which all variances were 1.0 and all intercorrelations were 0.5. The files ACOV.CM6, ACOV.KM6, and ACOV.PM6 used in examples (a), (b), and (c), respectively, are files where the asymptotic covariance matrices are stored. These can be read directly by LISREL and used with the WLS option.

In Example 6A, we estimate:

1. variances and covariances of the variables using normal scores for the ordinal variables,
2. the asymptotic covariance matrix of these variances and covariances. and
3. the relative multivariate kurtosis.

Complete output for this example follows.

```
EXAMPLE 6A: TESTING ASYMPTOTIC VARIANCES AND COVARIANCES   MA=CM
DA NI=5;RA=DATA.EX6;CO 1 2;NS 3 4 5;OU MA=CM SA=ACOV.CM6 PA
```

Total Sample Size =   200

Univariate Summary Statistics for Continuous Variables

Variable	Mean	St. Dev.	T-Value	Skewness	Kurtosis	Minimum	Freq.	Maximum	Freq.
VAR 1	0.084	1.042	1.140	0.035	0.021	-2.920	1	3.040	1
VAR 2	0.010	1.015	0.137	0.166	0.830	-2.850	1	4.060	1
VAR 3	0.000	0.797	0.000	-0.244	-1.961	-0.896	88	0.704	112
VAR 4	0.000	0.892	0.000	-0.247	-1.345	-1.320	46	0.966	80
VAR 5	0.000	0.924	0.000	-0.154	-1.274	-1.372	42	1.118	64

Relative Multivariate Kurtosis = 0.933

Covariance Matrix

	VAR 1	VAR 2	VAR 3	VAR 4	VAR 5
VAR 1	1.086				
VAR 2	0.498	1.030			
VAR 3	0.328	0.314	0.635		
VAR 4	0.394	0.319	0.287	0.796	
VAR 5	0.443	0.424	0.297	0.364	0.854

Asymptotic Covariance Matrix of Variances and Covariances

	S(1,1)	S(2,1)	S(2,2)	S(3,1)	S(3,2)	S(3,3)
S(1,1)	0.01179					
S(2,1)	0.00368	0.00642				
S(2,2)	0.00211	0.00704	0.01482			
S(3,1)	0.00292	0.00164	0.00080	0.00282		
S(3,2)	0.00076	0.00170	0.00302	0.00106	0.00270	
S(3,3)	-0.00005	0.00000	-0.00005	0.00006	0.00006	0.00012
S(4,1)	0.00489	0.00237	0.00162	0.00149	0.00049	0.00007
S(4,2)	0.00163	0.00284	0.00444	0.00059	0.00145	0.00004
S(4,3)	0.00059	0.00040	0.00049	0.00084	0.00059	0.00005
S(4,4)	0.00113	0.00027	0.00039	0.00021	0.00001	0.00004
S(5,1)	0.00481	0.00238	0.00190	0.00156	0.00036	0.00006
S(5,2)	0.00119	0.00312	0.00519	0.00036	0.00136	-0.00006
S(5,3)	0.00068	0.00031	0.00051	0.00097	0.00081	0.00005
S(5,4)	0.00172	0.00077	0.00124	0.00029	0.00030	0.00002
S(5,5)	0.00080	0.00027	0.00060	0.00000	0.00015	0.00005

Asymptotic Covariance Matrix of Variances and Covariances

	S(4,1)	S(4,2)	S(4,3)	S(4,4)	S(5,1)	S(5,2)
S(4,1)	0.00465					
S(4,2)	0.00161	0.00395				
S(4,3)	0.00095	0.00079	0.00214			
S(4,4)	0.00118	0.00097	0.00070	0.00210		
S(5,1)	0.00282	0.00097	0.00025	0.00049	0.00442	
S(5,2)	0.00084	0.00243	0.00026	0.00018	0.00145	0.00407
S(5,3)	0.00030	0.00040	0.00075	0.00008	0.00074	0.00085
S(5,4)	0.00153	0.00128	0.00073	0.00091	0.00145	0.00122
S(5,5)	0.00059	0.00063	-0.00006	0.00051	0.00129	0.00120

Asymptotic Covariance Matrix of Variances and Covariances

	S(5,3)	S(5,4)	S(5,5)
S(5,3)	0.00229		
S(5,4)	0.00062	0.00322	
S(5,5)	0.00077	0.00103	0.00267

The covariance matrix has 15 independent elements, so the asymptotic covariance matrix of these 15 elements is a symmetric matrix of order 15 × 15.

The lower half of this matrix, including the diagonal, contains 15 × 16/2 elements and is printed in sections.

The matrix stored in the file named ACOV.CM6 is equal to N times the asymptotic covariance printed in the output file (N is the sample size; in this case, $N = 200$). It is in binary form for maximum accuracy.

To obtain WLS estimates with LISREL, one needs only include the command AC=ACOV.CM6 in the command file. One can also use this file to obtain correct standard errors and chi-squares of ML-estimates under non-normality, see Jöreskog et alii (1999, Chapter 3).

4.9 Estimating asymptotic variances and covariances, MA=KM

In Example 6B, we estimate the correlations of the variables, still using normal scores for the ordinal variables, and the asymptotic covariance matrix of these correlations. Here, we give only those parts of the output which differ from the previous example.

```
EXAMPLE 6B: TESTING ASYMPTOTIC VARIANCES AND COVARIANCES  MA=KM
DA NI=5;RA=DATA.EX6;CO 1 2;NS 3 4 5;OU MA=KM SA=ACOV.KM6 PA
```

Correlation Matrix

	VAR 1	VAR 2	VAR 3	VAR 4	VAR 5
VAR 1	1.000				
VAR 2	0.471	1.000			
VAR 3	0.395	0.388	1.000		
VAR 4	0.424	0.352	0.403	1.000	
VAR 5	0.460	0.452	0.403	0.442	1.000

Asymptotic Covariance Matrix of Correlations

	R(2,1)	R(3,1)	R(3,2)	R(4,1)	R(4,2)	R(4,3)
R(2,1)	0.00273					
R(3,1)	0.00080	0.00317				
R(3,2)	0.00039	0.00126	0.00321			
R(4,1)	0.00081	0.00067	0.00022	0.00336		
R(4,2)	0.00099	0.00033	0.00090	0.00096	0.00323	
R(4,3)	0.00021	0.00122	0.00089	0.00086	0.00075	0.00383
R(5,1)	0.00072	0.00077	-0.00006	0.00138	0.00028	0.00016
R(5,2)	0.00100	0.00016	0.00055	0.00031	0.00124	0.00029
R(5,3)	0.00005	0.00141	0.00118	0.00013	0.00033	0.00142
R(5,4)	0.00012	0.00007	0.00016	0.00107	0.00094	0.00090

Asymptotic Covariance Matrix of Correlations

	R(5,1)	R(5,2)	R(5,3)	R(5,4)
R(5,1)	0.00275			
R(5,2)	0.00057	0.00249		
R(5,3)	0.00044	0.00072	0.00386	
R(5,4)	0.00090	0.00080	0.00062	0.00389

The correlation matrix has 10 estimated correlations, so the asymptotic covariance matrix of these has $.5 \times 10 \times 11 = 55$ independent elements. Note that the variances of the correlations are smaller than the variances of the corresponding covariances.

4.10 Estimating asymptotic variances and covariances, MA=PM

In Example 6C, we use the PM specification to estimate polychoric and polyserial correlations between the variables, and the asymptotic variances and covariances of these. We give only the parts of the output that differ from the previous two examples.

```
EXAMPLE 6C: TESTING ASYMPTOTIC VARIANCES AND COVARIANCES  MA=PM
DA NI=5;RA=DATA.EX6;CO 1 2;OU MA=PM SA=ACOV.PM6 PA
```

Bivariate Distributions for Ordinal Variables (Frequencies)

```
            VAR 4           VAR 5
         --------------  -------------------
VAR 3    1    2    3     1    2    3    4
         --------------  -------------------
1        33   38   17    30   28   16   14
2        13   36   63    12   15   35   50


            VAR 5
         -------------------
VAR 4    1    2    3    4
         -------------------
1        21   11   8    6
2        13   25   21   15
3        8    7    22   43
```

Bivariate Summary Statistics for Pairs of Variables
(The First Variable is Ordinal and the Second is Continuous)

```
    VAR 3 vs.    VAR 1
    --------     --------
Category   Number of Observations   Mean   Standard Deviation
--------   ----------------------   ----   ------------------
   1                88             -0.379        0.892
   2               112              0.448        1.010


    VAR 3 vs.    VAR 2
    --------     --------
Category   Number of Observations   Mean   Standard Deviation
--------   ----------------------   ----   ------------------
   1                88             -0.433        0.872
   2               112              0.358        0.986
```

```
VAR 4 vs.    VAR 1
--------     --------
Category  Number of Observations   Mean  Standard Deviation
--------  ----------------------   ----  ------------------
   1                46            -0.652        1.071
   2                74             0.072        0.854
   3                80             0.518        0.950


VAR 4 vs.    VAR 2
--------     --------
Category  Number of Observations   Mean  Standard Deviation
--------  ----------------------   ----  ------------------
   1                46            -0.594        0.928
   2                74             0.010        0.950
   3                80             0.357        0.967


VAR 5 vs.    VAR 1
--------     --------
Category  Number of Observations   Mean  Standard Deviation
--------  ----------------------   ----  ------------------
   1                42            -0.621        0.942
   2                43            -0.280        0.929
   3                51             0.297        0.856
   4                64             0.621        0.971


VAR 5 vs.    VAR 2
--------     --------
Category  Number of Observations   Mean  Standard Deviation
--------  ----------------------   ----  ------------------
   1                42            -0.571        0.826
   2                43            -0.328        1.069
   3                51             0.001        0.706
   4                64             0.625        0.982
```

Correlations and Test Statistics

(PE=Pearson Product Moment, PC=Polychoric, PS=Polyserial)

Variable vs. Variable	Correlation	Test of Model Chi-Squ.	D.F.	P-Value	Test of Close Fit RMSEA	P-Value
VAR 2 vs. VAR 1	0.471 (PE)					
VAR 3 vs. VAR 1	0.500 (PS)	1.306	1	0.253	0.039	0.364
VAR 3 vs. VAR 2	0.491 (PS)	1.273	1	0.259	0.037	0.370
VAR 4 vs. VAR 1	0.481 (PS)	3.726	3	0.293	0.035	0.493
VAR 4 vs. VAR 2	0.395 (PS)	1.224	3	0.747	0.000	0.859
VAR 4 vs. VAR 3	0.544 (PC)	0.409	1	0.522	0.000	0.616
VAR 5 vs. VAR 1	0.502 (PS)	2.595	5	0.762	0.000	0.898
VAR 5 vs. VAR 2	0.492 (PS)	11.051	5	0.050	0.078	0.190
VAR 5 vs. VAR 3	0.531 (PC)	3.661	2	0.160	0.064	0.303
VAR 5 vs. VAR 4	0.532 (PC)	7.096	5	0.214	0.046	0.460

Correlation Matrix

	VAR 1	VAR 2	VAR 3	VAR 4	VAR 5
VAR 1	1.000				
VAR 2	0.471	1.000			
VAR 3	0.500	0.491	1.000		
VAR 4	0.481	0.395	0.544	1.000	
VAR 5	0.502	0.492	0.531	0.532	1.000

Asymptotic Covariance Matrix of Correlations

	R(2,1)	R(3,1)	R(3,2)	R(4,1)	R(4,2)	R(4,3)
R(2,1)	0.00273					
R(3,1)	0.00042	0.01457				
R(3,2)	-0.00044	0.00716	0.01418			
R(4,1)	0.00056	0.01711	0.00903	0.02627		
R(4,2)	0.00015	0.00820	0.01729	0.01418	0.02655	
R(4,3)	0.00000	-0.00339	-0.00346	-0.00644	-0.00467	0.01329
R(5,1)	0.00086	0.02186	0.01007	0.03060	0.01402	-0.01095
R(5,2)	0.00070	0.01050	0.02110	0.01663	0.03002	-0.01007
R(5,3)	-0.00010	-0.00363	-0.00316	-0.00620	-0.00352	0.01414
R(5,4)	0.00022	-0.00438	-0.00408	-0.01201	-0.00820	0.02289

Asymptotic Covariance Matrix of Correlations

	R(5,1)	R(5,2)	R(5,3)	R(5,4)
R(5,1)	0.04923			
R(5,2)	0.02816	0.04934		
R(5,3)	-0.01216	-0.01022	0.01681	
R(5,4)	-0.02229	-0.02106	0.02399	0.05032

All polychoric and polyserial correlations are closer to the true value 0.5 *than were the corresponding product-moment correlations in Example 6B.*

The product-moment correlation (2,1) has a smaller variance than the polychoric correlations (4,3), (5,3), and (5,4) which in turn have smaller variances than the polyserial correlations. Note that the variances of the polychoric and polyserial correlations tend to get smaller as the number of categories increases.

A Warnings and error messages

Warnings and error messages in the printout are usually self-explanatory. Recommended solutions are provided on the following pages, where the three kinds of messages are listed in order of their three-digit error codes.

☐ SYNTAX ERROR (three digit codes starting with 1)

A PRELIS command has been incorrectly entered (invalid characters were used and/or were entered in the wrong order). All syntax errors in the input file will be pointed out, and the program will not run this problem. The next problem (if any) will proceed. *See Chapter 2 and the appropriate command descriptions in Chapter 3.*

☐ WARNING (three digit codes starting with 2)

Attention is called to a particular condition that does not immediately lead to a complete program stop, but may eventually lead to a fatal error, for example, a variance of 0, or a correlation of $+1$ or -1.

☐ FATAL ERROR (three digit codes starting with 3)

Stop processing the current problem; proceed to next problem, if any.

☐ FATAL ERROR (three digit codes starting with 4)

Any one of these conditions will cause a complete program stop:

- there is no DA command in the input file
- NI is not specified on the DA command
- there is no RA command in the input file
- no data file was specified on the RA command

- *filename* specified on the RA line does not exist
- a command with a non-valid command name has been found
- there is no OU command in the input file.
- incorrect format for raw data
- illegal character in the raw data

A.1   Syntax errors

101 SYNTAX ERROR: x IS NOT A VALID PARAMETER NAME

You have used the non-valid keyword or option x in one of your PRELIS commands. The line with the non-valid keyword or option appears immediately before the error message.

Check the proper syntax in Chapter 3.

102 SYNTAX ERROR: A NON-VALID VALUE SPECIFIED x

You have given an incorrect numeric value x in an MI, PO, LO, or RE command. A numeric value must be of one of three possible forms:

1) an integer, such as ± 17
2) a decimal number, such as ± 17.35
3) a number in scientific notation, such as $\pm 1.735E \pm 13$ or $\pm 1.735D \pm 13$,

where $\pm$ means either $+$ or $-$ or nothing.

Note: blanks are not permitted; and no characters are permitted other than the ten digits and the characters $+$, $-$, ., D, and E.

This error will also occur if you assign an incorrect character value to the TR or MA parameter.

103 SYNTAX ERROR: VARIABLE LABEL x IS NOT DEFINED.

You are referring to variable x in a *varlist* before its label has been defined in the LA command.

104 SYNTAX ERROR: VARIABLE NUMBER x IS NOT DEFINED.

You are referring to a variable by the number x, where x is either less than 1 or larger than the number of variables.

See page 59.

105 SYNTAX ERROR: MORE THAN TEN RG LINES IN THE INPUT FILE.

Only ten RG commands are permitted in the command file. If this error occurs, only regressions requested on the first ten RG commands will be estimated.

See page 90.

106 SYNTAX ERROR: KEYWORD x NOT FOUND.

There is a required keyword on the command listed just before the error in the output that was not specified. Check the syntax description for the command in Chapter 3 against your command file.

A.2 Warning messages

201 WARNING: x has more than 15 categories and will be treated as continuous.

The variable x, which is ordinal (either by your specification or by default) has more than the maximum 15 distinct values, not counting missing values.

See page 59.

If you are satisfied with treating this variable as continuous, nothing needs to be done. But if you really want to treat this variable as ordinal, you can use RE commands to recode the variable into fewer categories.

202 WARNING: Variable x has no cases in category z in the contingency table with variable y. The column will be deleted in the computation of the polychoric correlation.

The contingency table between the ordinal variables x and y has one empty column corresponding to category z of x. Although there are cases in category z in the univariate distribution of x, these cases have been eliminated in the bivariate distribution because all have missing values on variable y when pairwise deletion is used.

The polychoric correlation can still be computed, provided there are at least two non-empty categories on both variables. If this is not the case, fatal error 306 will appear and processing of this problem will stop.

See page 24.

203 WARNING: Variable x has no cases in category z in the contingency table with variable y. The row will be deleted in the computation of the polychoric correlation.

The contingency table between the ordinal variables x and y has one empty row corresponding to category z of x. Although there are cases in category z in the univariate distribution of x, these cases have been eliminated in the bivariate distribution because all have missing values on variable y when pairwise deletion is used.

The polychoric correlation can still be computed provided there are at least two non-empty categories on both variables. If this is not the case, fatal error 306 will appear and processing of this problem will stop.

See page 24.

204 WARNING: Category x has been deleted in the computation of the polyserial correlation because of zero within variance.

When this warning appears, the context will indicate the pair of variables for which polyserial correlation is being computed. Either there is only a single case in category x, or the values of the continuous variable corresponding to category x of the ordinal variable are all equal, and the variance of the continuous variable given category x of the ordinal variable is, therefore, zero. This category cannot be used in the computation of the polyserial correlation. (Recall that a polyserial correlation is a correlation between an ordinal and a continuous variable.)

The polyserial correlation can still be computed, if there are at least two categories of the ordinal variable for which the within variance is positive. If this is not the case, fatal error 307 will appear.

See page 25.

205 WARNING: The iterations did not converge. The correlation may not be correct.

This warning should not occur. It means that the program has not been able to estimate a polychoric or polyserial correlation for a pair of variables. The context in which the warning appears will indicate the pair of variables and the type of correlation involved.

The message is probably the result of a too-small (pairwise) sample and data that are inconsistent with assumptions underlying the polychoric and polyserial correlations.

See pages 24–25.

206 WARNING: The correlation is unity. Check your data.

The estimated correlation for a pair of variables is ± 1. This may be unreasonable, so check your data. The pair of variables causing the problem will be clear from the context in which this message appears.

207 WARNING: Power or log transformation is not possible for case z of variable x because AL + BE*x = y.

You have to think about what the transformation means in relation to the variable x. In the formula $\alpha + \beta x = y$, x is the value the variable x takes for case z.

Warning 207 has occurred for one of these reasons:
  ○ y^{γ} is not defined, or
  ○ $\log(y)$ is not defined.

The program will continue until all cases have been read, noting all cases for which the transformation is not possible. It will then print fatal error 303, which leads to a problem stop.

See page 70.

208 WARNING: Covariance matrix not positive-definite for the variables: *varlist*.

You have requested estimated regression(s) with one or more RG commands. The covariance, correlation, or moment matrix for the variables in *varlist* is not positive-definite. As a result, one or more of the requested regressions cannot be estimated.

See page 90.

The root of the problem may be:
  ○ one or more of the variables in *varlist* is a linear combination of the other variables, or
  ○ the sample size is smaller than the number of variables in *varlist*.

209 WARNING: The asymptotic covariance matrix of estimated coefficients can only be estimated under listwise deletion.

You have requested SA=*filename* with TR=PA. Change to listwise deletion: TR=LI.

See page 97.

210 WARNING: The asymptotic covariance matrix of estimated coefficients is not available when MA=MM, MA=AM, or MA=OM.

See page 97.

211 WARNING: The asymptotic variances of estimated coefficients can only be estimated under listwise deletion.

You have requested SV=*filename* with TR=PA. Change to listwise deletion: TR=LI.

See page 97.

212 WARNING: The asymptotic variances of estimated coefficients is not available when MA=MM, MA=AM, or MA=OM.

See page 97.

213 WARNING: The asymptotic covariance matrix of estimated coefficients can only be printed if a file has been specified with SA.

You have requested PA without including SA=*filename*.

See page 94.

214 WARNING: The asymptotic variances of estimated coefficients can only be printed if a file has been specified with SV.

You have requested PV without including SV=*filename*.

See page 94.

215 WARNING: Sample size too small. Asymptotic variances and covariances will not be computed.

You have requested SA=*filename* or SV=*filename*, but your sample size is too small for these options.

See page 171.

If you really need to compute asymptotic variances and/or covariances, you should add more cases.

216 WARNING: Error(s) occurred when computing asymptotic covariances. Asymptotic covariance matrix not computed.

The method for computing asymptotic variances and covariances requires that certain matrices be positive-definite.

This error usually occurs when your sample is too small or your data are otherwise inadequate.

See page 171.

217 WARNING: The Relative Multivariate Kurtosis measure is only available for TR=LI and MA=CM.

You have requested PK without specifying TR=LI or MA=CM.

218 WARNING: The estimated covariance matrix is not positive-definite. The Relative Multivariate Kurtosis cannot be computed.

There are two possible causes.

- ○ one (or more) of your variables is a linear combination of other variables, or
- ○ the sample size is smaller than the number of variables.

Data of this kind are all right, but they cannot be used to compute Mardia's measure of relative multivariate kurtosis (which you have requested by specifying the PK option).

219 WARNING: x has only one value.

All cases have the same value on variable x (missing values excluded). This may have been caused by selection (SC or SD) or recoding (RE).

See pages 62, 72, and 75.

If you have also specified MA=KM, MA=OM, or MA=PM, fatal error 304 will occur.

220 WARNING: No varlist specified in line above.

The command given just before this warning in the output lacks the proper and required specification of a *varlist*. Check your syntax.

A.3 Fatal errors: problem stop

301 FATAL ERROR: SYNTAX ERROR(S) FOUND. PROBLEM NOT RUN.

One or more syntax errors were found in the command file. These syntax errors are pointed out individually. All syntax errors must be corrected before the run is tried again.

302 FATAL ERROR: SAMPLE SIZE TOO SMALL FOR POLYCHORIC AND POLY-SERIAL CORRELATIONS. PROBLEM NOT COMPLETED.

You have requested MA=PM with either

- ○ a listwise sample size less than 20, or
- ○ a pairwise sample size less than 20 for at least one pair of variables.

Sample sizes less than 20 are really much too small to be able to estimate polychoric and/or polyserial correlations.

303 FATAL ERROR: TRANSFORMATION ERROR(S) OCCURRED IN x CASE(s). PROBLEM NOT RUN.

For x cases, the transformation(s) you requested on your PO or LO command(s) were not defined. The values of $\alpha + \beta x$ for these cases are listed separately in the warning message 207. You have to think about what each transformation means in relation to your data.

See page 70.

304 FATAL ERROR: x HAS ONLY ONE VALUE. PROBLEM NOT COMPLETED.

The variable x has only one value, not counting missing values. The variance of this variable is, therefore, zero. The correlation matrix cannot be computed when this variable is included. You may use an SD command to delete this variable.

See page 75.

305 FATAL ERROR: TOO FEW CASES SELECTED. PROBLEM NOT RUN.

The condition(s) specified on an SC or an SD command is such that not enough cases satisfy it. After selection, the effective sample size is too small. Change your *conditionlist*.

See pages 72 and 75.

306 FATAL ERROR: VARIABLE x HAS LESS THAN TWO CATEGORIES FOR VARIABLE y. POLYCHORIC CORRELATION CANNOT BE COMPUTED. PROBLEM NOT COMPLETED.

The contingency table for variables x and y has only one row or only one column. This makes it impossible to estimate a polychoric correlation. This error may occur as a consequence of warnings 202 or 203.

See page 24.

307 FATAL ERROR: ORDINAL VARIABLE x HAS LESS THAN TWO CATEGORIES FOR VARIABLE y. POLYSERIAL CORRELATION CANNOT BE COMPUTED. PROBLEM NOT COMPLETED.

The polyserial correlation between variables x and y cannot be computed because ordinal variable x has only one category. This error may occur as a consequence of warning 204.

See page 25.

308 FATAL ERROR: THE PROBLEM REQUIRES A WORKSPACE OF AT LEAST x BYTES. ONLY y IS AVAILABLE.

First check if your command file is correct. If it is correct, but you still get this message and:

o you are running PRELIS on a *personal computer*, you may need to install more memory before you can run this problem.

See page 36.

o if you are running PRELIS on a *mainframe*, contact the person who installed the program on the computer.

309 FATAL ERROR: IMPOSSIBLE TO COMPUTE POLYSERIAL CORRELATION BETWEEN x AND y. PROBABLY SOMETHING IS WRONG IN YOUR DATA OR DATA FORMAT. PROBLEM NOT COMPLETED.

This error should not occur. If it does, it is probably because something is wrong in your data. Check to be sure you have NI data values for each case. If you are reading data with a format, make sure the format is correct.

310 FATAL ERROR: EQUAL THRESHOLDS NOT AVAILABLE UNDER PAIRWISE DELE-TION. PROBLEM NOT COMPLETED.

The use of the ET command to estimate equal thresholds is not available with pairwise deletion (TR=PA) selected on the DA command. Switch to listwise deletion.

311 FATAL ERROR: EQUAL THRESHOLDS NOT POSSIBLE FOR x AND y, NUMBER OF CATEGORIES ARE NOT EQUAL. PROBLEM NOT COMPLETED.

The use of the ET command to estimate equal thresholds requires that the variables given in the *varlist* have the same number of categories. The pair of variables x and y fails that requirement.

312 FATAL ERROR: THRESHOLDS FOR x ARE NOT STRICTLY INCREASING. PROBLEM NOT COMPLETED.

The use of the ET command to estimate equal thresholds requires that thresholds for consecutive categories form a series of increasing numbers. Variable x fails that condition.

313 FATAL ERROR: BOOTSTRAPPING IS NOT AVAILABLE WITH FIXED-X. PROBLEM NOT COMPLETED.

You cannot use the FI command to declare certain variables x-variables with bootstrapping procedures.

314 FATAL ERROR: THE AVAILABLE WORKSPACE IS NOT LARGE ENOUGH FOR FIXED-X. PROBLEM NOT COMPLETED.

First check if your command file is correct. If it is correct, but you still get this message and:

o you are running PRELIS on a *personal computer*, you may need to install more memory before you can run this problem.

See page 36.

o if you are running PRELIS on a *mainframe*, contact the person who installed the program on the computer.

315 FATAL ERROR: FIXED-X CAN NOT BE USED WITH MA=x PROBLEM NOT COMPLETED.

Your OU command specifies MA=MM, MA=KM, MA=AM, MA=PM, or MA=OM. These types of moment matrices cannot be computed when the FI command (to declare x-variables) has also been given in the command file.

A.4   Fatal errors: program stop

401 FATAL ERROR: A DA LINE WAS EXPECTED BUT NOT FOUND. PROGRAM STOPPED.

No DA command followed immediately after the title.

See page 46.

402 FATAL ERROR: NI MUST BE SPECIFIED. PROGRAM STOPPED.

NI was not specified on the DA command. PRELIS must know the number of variables to be processed before it can proceed.

See page 48.

403 FATAL ERROR: CANNOT FIND THE FILE x. PROGRAM STOPPED.

PRELIS cannot find the data file referred to on the RA command.

o If you are running the PC version, check to see if you misspelled the filename or specified an incorrect directory.

o If you are running a mainframe version, check to see if you opened this file before PRELIS was invoked.

404 FATAL ERROR: x IS NOT A VALID LINE NAME. PROGRAM STOPPED.

You have used a non-valid command name in one of your PRELIS commands. The line with the error appears immediately before the error message.

See page 33 for a list of all valid command names.

405 FATAL ERROR: NO DATA FILE SPECIFIED. PROGRAM STOPPED.

You forgot to specify a data file on the RA command.

See page 55.

406 FATAL ERROR: UNEXPECTED END OF FILE IN FILE x.

An end-of-file was encountered before an OU command was found in your input file x.

See page 46.

407 FATAL ERROR: ERROR IN RAW DATA FOR CASE i. PROGRAM STOPPED.

An illegal character appears in the data vector for case i.

See page 56.

Recall that each data vector must consist of NI data values, each of which must be of three possible forms:

1) an integer, such as ±17
2) a decimal number, such as ±17.35
3) a number in scientific notation, such as $\pm1.735E \pm 13$ or $\pm1.735D \pm 13$,

where $\pm$ means either $+$ or $-$ or nothing.

Note: blanks are not permitted; and no characters are permitted other than the ten digits and the characters $+$, $-$, ., D, and E.

Common errors in data are:

- comma (,) entered for decimal point
- character 'o' entered for digit '0' (zero)
- two decimal points (periods) entered within the same format field

The data vector where the error has occurred will be printed just below this error message. If the error is in the j-th data value, this data vector contains the first $j - 1$ values for case i and the last NI$-j + 1$ values for case $i - 1$.

408 FATAL ERROR: PARENTHESES DO NOT MATCH IN FORMAT. PROGRAM STOPPED.

Each FORTRAN format begins with a left parenthesis and ends with a right parenthesis. Parentheses may also appear within the format, but for each left parenthesis there must be a right parenthesis. In other words, the total number of left parentheses must be the same as the total number of right parentheses.

APPENDIX A: WARNINGS AND ERROR MESSAGES

B   New features in PRELIS 2

B.1   Compatibility with PRELIS 1

Input

Every input file which runs on PRELIS 1 should run on PRELIS 2.[1] Note, however, the following differences.

- □ PRELIS 1 assumes that all variables are continuous by default, but PRELIS 2 assumes that all variables are ordinal by default. Thus, all variables which are measured on an interval scale should be declared continuous. See the sections *Data screening and summarization* (p. 145), *Variables and scale types* (p. 146), and *Multivariate multinomial probit regressions* (p. 178).

- □ The recode command and the syntax for specification of missing values have been extended, see the sections *Improvement of the recode command* (p. 150) and *Specification of missing values* (p. 152). Many commands for reading and saving matrices can be simplified, see the section *Simplified syntax for reading and saving matrices* (p. 158). All these changes have been made in such a way that the old versions of the same commands are still recognized.

- □ An exclamation mark (!) or the slash-asterisk combination (/*) may be used to indicate that everything that follows on this line is to be regarded as comments. Blank (empty) lines are still accepted without the ! or /*.

---

[1]The authors are grateful to Anne-Marie Aish for many useful suggestions in the development of PRELIS 2 and to Ed Rigdon for testing the program.

□ The first line for each problem may be a title line containing any information used as a heading for the problem. One may choose not to have a title line or use only a single title line. However, any number of title lines may be used to describe the model and the data. The program will read title lines until it finds a physical line whose first two non-blank characters are DA, Da, dA, or da, which is the first command line in a PRELIS input file. Therefore, one must not use title lines beginning with these characters. To avoid this conflict, one may begin every title line with an exclamation mark (!). Then, anything can appear on the title lines.

Title lines are optional but strongly recommended. Only title lines can appear before the first genuine command line.

□ To run stacked input (*i.e.*, several problems in the same input file) based on the same raw data, one must rewind[2] the file containing the raw data after each use, *i.e.*, one must specify the RE (for rewind) option on the RA command. This was not necessary in PRELIS 1 as the file containing the raw data was always rewound after each use. The reason for this change is that PRELIS 2 stores the raw data in memory whenever possible.

Output

The output from PRELIS 2 gives more information than PRELIS 1 and the information is presented better (see the section *Frequencies, percentages, bar charts, histograms*, p. 148). Also, because of new and better estimation theory for asymptotic covariance matrices, some of these are different from PRELIS 1, see the section *Asymptotic covariance matrices* (p. 167). PRELIS 2 has many new features as described in the following sections.

B.2 Faster execution

PRELIS 2 runs faster than PRELIS 1 because the data matrix is stored in memory if there is room for it in the available workspace. This means

---

[2]The term *rewind* stems from 'mainframe' days when data were read from a file on tape. To process such a file again, the tape had to be rewound to the start of the file.

that reading the data in the second and third pass is faster. If there is not sufficient memory in the workspace to store the entire raw data, it will be read from the file in each pass, as in PRELIS 1.

B.3 Data screening and summarization

Most raw data for analyses have been recorded and stored on media like diskettes or tapes or downloaded from large files at data archives. The raw data file may contain many variables on many cases. Before doing more elaborate analysis of the data, it is important to do a careful data screening to check for coding errors or other mistakes in the data. Such data screening will also give a general idea of the character and quality of the data.

PRELIS 2 automatically does such data screening by determining for each variable the distinct data values present in the data and the number of each. If a variable has more than 15 distinct values, PRELIS 2 will group them in intervals and determine the number in each interval.

Example 7A: Data screening

The file EX7.RAW contains many variables on a subset of cases from the first cross-section of a political action survey (Barnes & Kaase, 1979). The following input file (EX7A.PR2) does data screening of the six political efficacy items (see Aish & Jöreskog, 1990) from this file.

```
!EXAMPLE 7A
!Data Screening of Six Political Efficacy Items in File EX7.RAW
DA NI=6                          ! Note: Sample Size is unknown
LA
NOSAY VOTING COMPLEX NOCARE TOUCH INTEREST
RA=EX7.RAW FO                    ! Note this simplified syntax
(141X,6F2.0)
OU
```

This is the simplest form of raw data screening. For each variable, PRELIS 2 lists all data values found in the raw data, the number and relative frequency of each data value, and it gives a bar chart showing the distribution of the data values. For NOSAY this looks as follows.

```
NOSAY Frequency Percentage Bar Chart
  1      38       12.2     **********
  2      89       28.5     **************************
  3     159       51.0     **************************************************
  4      21        6.7     ******
  8       5        1.6     *
```

The numbers on the left are the data values that PRELIS 2 found in the data. For NOSAY the values 1, 2, 3, 4, and 8 were found. No value 9 was found. For all the other variables, there are values 1, 2, 3, 4, 8, and 9 in the data. See the section *Labels for categories* (p. 147) on how to assign category labels to the data values representing ordered categories.

B.4 Variables and scale types

A fundamental principle in PRELIS is the distinction between variables of different scale types. PRELIS 2 distinguishes between the following type of variables: continuous, ordinal, censored, and fixed. Ordinal, censored, and fixed variables require quite different treatment than continuous variables. Fixed variables are defined in the section *Multivariate multinomial probit regressions* (p. 178).

Observations on an ordinal variable are assumed to represent responses to a set of ordered categories, such as a five-category Likert scale. It is only assumed that a person who responds in one category has more of a characteristic than a person who responds in a lower category. Ordinal variables are not continuous variables and should not be treated as if they are. It is common practice to treat scores 1, 2, 3, ... assigned to categories as if they have interval scale properties. Ordinal variables do not have origins or units of measurements. Means, variances, and covariances of ordinal variables have no meaning. The only information we have are counts of cases in each cell of a multiway contingency table. To use ordinal variables in structural equation models requires other techniques than those that are traditionally employed with continuous variables. Jöreskog & Aish (1996) give further details on the treatment of ordinal variables and several applications of structural equation models with ordinal variables.

The classification of variables is normally done with OR, CO, CE, CA, CB, or FI commands listing those variables which are ordinal, continuous, censored, censored above, censored below, and fixed, respectively. However, if this is *not* done, PRELIS 2 will classify the variables as follows. All variables with less than 16 distinct values are classified as ordinal. All other variables are classified as continuous. The MC keyword in PRELIS 1 is no longer supported.

B.5 Labels for categories

One can specify labels (names) for categories of categorical (ordinal) variables. This makes it easier to read and interpret univariate and bivariate distributions of categorical (ordinal) variables. The syntax for doing this is

```
CL varlist n1=clab1 n2=clab2 ...
```

where *varlist* is a list of variables by labels or numbers (see examples on page 60 above), n1, n2, ... are the numerical values in the data on these variables, and clab1, clab2, ... are the labels to be assigned to these numerical values. Each category label may contain up to four characters.

Example 7B: Assigning labels to categories

The following input file (EX7B.PR2) will read the six political efficacy items from the file EX7.RAW and assign category labels AS, A, D, DS, DK, and NA to the numerical values 1, 2, 3, 4, 8, and 9, respectively (AS = Agree Strongly, A = Agree, D = Disagree, DS = Disagree Strongly, DK = Don't Know, NA = No Answer).

```
EXAMPLE 7B
!Assigning Category Labels as follows
!AS = Agree Strongly, A = Agree, D = Disagree, DS = Disagree Strongly,
!DK = Don't Know, NA = No Answer
DA NI=6
LA;NOSAY VOTING COMPLEX NOCARE TOUCH INTEREST  ! Note the ;
RA=EX7.RAW FO;(141X,6F2.0)                      ! Note the ;
CL NOSAY - INTEREST 1=AS 2=A 3=D 4=DS 8=DK 9=NA
OU
```

Note that one must know which numerical values are present in the data to do this. If these are unknown, screen the data first, as demonstrated in the section *Data screening and summarization* (p. 145).

Each CL command contains a *varlist* listing all variables with the same category labels, followed by a listing defining category labels for numerical values. If the category labels do not fit on a line of 127 characters, repeat the same CL command and *varlist* and continue with the remaining category labels. If the *varlist* on the CL command is too long to fit on one line of 127 characters, write the remaining variables in *varlist* on a new CL command followed by the same list of category labels as for the previous CL command.

Important note: If some of the variables are recoded, the category labels refer to the recoded values.

B.6   Frequencies, percentages, bar charts, histograms

For both univariate and bivariate distributions of categorical (ordinal) variables, frequencies are given in absolute as well as relative form (percentages). In addition, bar charts representing the univariate marginal distribution are given for each ordinal variable. For continuous variables, PRELIS 2 gives a histogram in addition to the statistics given in PRELIS 1. Tests of univariate and multivariate normality are also given for continuous variables (see the section *Tests of univariate and multivariate normality*, p. 166).

The output for Example 7B illustrates this:

```
Univariate Distributions for Ordinal Variables

  NOSAY Frequency Percentage Bar Chart
     AS        38       12.2  **********
      A        89       28.5  *************************
      D       159       51.0  ***********************************************
     DS        21        6.7  ******
     DK         5        1.6  *
```

```
VOTING  Frequency  Percentage  Bar Chart
  AS        54        17.3     *****************
   A       141        45.2     *********************************************
   D        99        31.7     ********************************
  DS        10         3.2     ***
  DK         7         2.2     **
  NA         1         0.3

COMPLEX Frequency  Percentage  Bar Chart
  AS        83        26.6     ************************
   A       161        51.6     *************************************************
   D        53        17.0     ***************
  DS        12         3.8     ****
  DK         1         0.3
  NA         2         0.6     *

NOCARE  Frequency  Percentage  Bar Chart
  AS        45        14.4     ***************
   A       131        42.0     ******************************************
   D       118        37.8     *****************************************
  DS        11         3.5     ****
  DK         5         1.6     **
  NA         2         0.6     *

TOUCH   Frequency  Percentage  Bar Chart
  AS        49        15.7     *************
   A       161        51.6     *************************************************
   D        83        26.6     ***********************
  DS         5         1.6     *
  DK        10         3.2     ***
  NA         4         1.3     *

INTEREST Frequency Percentage  Bar Chart
  AS        46        14.7     **************
   A       143        45.8     *********************************************
   D       101        32.4     ********************************
  DS         8         2.6     ***
  DK        13         4.2     ****
  NA         1         0.3
```

B.7   Extension of the select cases command

The syntax for the SC (Select Cases) command has been extended as follows:

SC   *casecondition*

where *casecondition* is one of the following:

```
case < 300
case > 150
case = odd
case = even
```

These will select the first 299 cases, the cases 151, 152, ..., N (*i.e.*, all cases with case numbers above 150), all odd-numbered cases, all even-numbered cases, respectively. All analyses will be made on the subset of selected cases. This option is useful, for example, to select a random sub-sample of cases to be used for exploration versus cross-validation or other studies of sampling variability (see Jöreskog & Aish, 1996). A random subsample of any size can also be obtained by bootstrap sampling (see the section *Bootstrap estimates*, p. 171).

The *casecondition* can be used in combination with conditions on the values of variables as follows:

```
SC casecondition
SC varlist conditionlist
```

This selects all cases which satisfy *both* the *casecondition and all* conditions in the *conditionlist* for the variables in *varlist*. Only these selected cases will be used in the analysis. For example, if GENDER is coded 1 for males and 2 for females,

```
SC case=odd
SC GENDER =2
```

will select all females with odd case numbers (note the space between GENDER (the *varlist*) and =2 (the *conditionlist*).

B.8   Improvement of the recode command

The six efficacy items in Example 7B go from high agreement to low agreement, since *1 = Agree Strongly* and *4 = Disagree Strongly*. Suppose we wish to change the scale so that it goes from low to high. Because the recode command in PRELIS 1 has immediate effect, one had to do this as:

```
RE NOSAY - INTEREST OLD=1 NEW=40
RE NOSAY - INTEREST OLD=2 NEW=30
RE NOSAY - INTEREST OLD=3 NEW=20
RE NOSAY - INTEREST OLD=4 NEW=10
```

For neatness, one may also want to change the numbers 10 20 30 40 back to 1 2 3 4 by adding four more RE commands:

```
RE NOSAY - INTEREST OLD=10 NEW=1
RE NOSAY - INTEREST OLD=20 NEW=2
RE NOSAY - INTEREST OLD=30 NEW=3
RE NOSAY - INTEREST OLD=40 NEW=4
```

After these recodings, the scale goes from low to high, with $1 = Disagree$ $Strongly$ and $4 = Agree\ Strongly$. With PRELIS 2, one can do all this with a single recode command as:

```
RE NOSAY - INTEREST OLD=1,2,3,4 NEW=4,3,2,1
```

Suppose, we wish to dichotomize the variables by collapsing the two agree categories and the two disagree categories and at the same time recode the scale so that it goes from low to high. This can be done simply as:

```
RE NOSAY - INTEREST OLD=1-2,3-4 NEW=1,0
```

After this recoding, $0 = disagree$ and $1 = agree$.

The general syntax for the recode command is:

```
RE varlist OLD=a,b,c,... NEW=x,y,z,...
```

where each of a,b,c,... are either single values or a range of values of the form d-e, where d is smaller than e, and each of x,y,z,... are single values.

As in PRELIS 1, the recode command can be applied not only to ordinal variables but also to continuous variables. For example, a continuous income variable ranging from 50 to 500 (in hundreds of dollars, say) may be converted to a discrete variable with five income classes, as follows:

```
RE INCOME OLD=50-80,81-150,151-250,251-350,351-500 NEW=1,2,3,4,5
```

B.9 Specification of missing values

The specification of missing values has been greatly improved. PRELIS 1 allowed only one missing value for each variable. If there were several values to be treated as missing, one could always get around this problem by specifying one of them to be the missing value and then recoding all the other values to this value. This is somewhat inconvenient, and in PRELIS 2, one can specify several missing values directly.

To specify several values to be treated as missing in *all variables globally*, put MI=a,b,c on the DA command. To assign several missing values to a *specific set of variables*, write an MI command as follows.

```
MI=a,b,c,... varlist
```

where *varlist* is a list of variables and a,b,c,... are numerical values to be treated as missing values. If there is more than one missing value, there must be commas between the values, but not after the last missing value. Each of a,b,c,... can be one of the following:

- ❑ A single value
- ❑ A range of values from x to y inclusive, denoted x-y

Example 7C: Listwise deletion of missing values

The following input file (EX7C.PR2) reads the same data as in Example 7B and eliminates all cases with missing data. Category labels are then assigned to the data values that remain after listwise deletion and the data screening is done on this subsample.

```
EXAMPLE 7C
Listwise Elimination of Missing Values (DK and NA Responses)
DA NI=6 MI=8,9
LA;NOSAY VOTING COMPLEX NOCARE TOUCH INTEREST  !Note the ;
RA FI=EX7.RAW FO;(141X,6F2.0)                  !Note the ;
CL NOSAY - INTEREST 1=AS 2=A 3=D 4=DS
OU
```

The following tables in the output file give information about how the missing values are distributed over variables and cases.

```
Number of Missing Values per Variable
     NOSAY    VOTING   COMPLEX    NOCARE    TOUCH   INTEREST
        5         8         3         7       14         14

Distribution of Missing Values
Total Sample Size =     312
Number of Missing Values      0     1     2     3     4
          Number of Cases   282    18     5     5     2
```

Of the 312 cases in the data, there are only 282 without missing values, so this is the listwise sample on which the data screening is done. Note that there are 2 cases which are missing on 4 out of 6 variables.

B.10   Imputation of missing values

In PRELIS 1 there are two ways of handling missing values: pairwise and listwise deletion. In many situations, particularly when values are missing not completely at random, these procedures are far from satisfactory (see, for example, Little & Rubin, 1987, and Rubin, 1987). PRELIS 2 offers yet another possibility of handling missing values, namely by imputation, *i.e.*, by substitution of real values for the missing values. The value to be substituted for the missing value for a case is obtained from another case that has a similar response pattern over a set of matching variables. To do this, include a line

IM (*Ivarlist*) (*Mvarlist*) VR=n XN XL

in the input file, where *Ivarlist* is a set of variables whose missing values should be imputed and *Mvarlist* is a set of matching variables. VR, XN, and XL are explained below.

The imputation scheme is as follows. Let $y_1, y_2, \ldots, y_p$ denote the variables in *Ivarlist* and let $x_1, x_2, \ldots, x_q$ denote the variables in *Mvarlist*. To begin, let us assume that there is only a single variable y in *Ivarlist* whose missing values are to be imputed and that y is not included in *Mvarlist*. Let $z_1, z_2, \ldots, z_q$ be the standardized $x_1, x_2, \ldots, x_q$, *i.e.*, for each case c

$$z_{cj} = (x_{cj} - \bar{x}_j)/s_j \qquad j = 1, 2, \ldots, q \; ,$$

where $\bar{x}_j$ and s_j are the estimated mean and standard deviation of x_j. These are estimated from all complete data on x_j.

The imputation procedure is as follows.

1. Find the first case a with a missing value on y and no missing values on $x_1, x_2, \ldots, x_q$. If no such case exists, imputation of y is impossible. Otherwise, proceed to impute the value y_a as follows.

2. Find *all* cases b which have no missing value on y and no missing values on $x_1, x_2, \ldots, x_q$, and which minimizes

$$\sum_{j=1}^{q} (z_{bj} - z_{aj})^2 . \tag{B.1}$$

3. Two cases will occur

   ❏ If there is a single case b satisfying 2, y_a is replaced by y_b.

   ❏ Otherwise, if there are $n > 1$ matching cases b *with the same minimum value* of (B.1), denote their y-values by $y_1^{(m)}, y_2^{(m)}, \ldots, y_n^{(m)}$. Let

$$\bar{y}_m = (1/n) \sum_{i=1}^{n} y_i^{(m)}, \ \ s_m^2 = [1/(n-1)]) \sum_{i=1}^{n} (y_i^{(m)} - \bar{y}_m)^2,$$

   be the mean and variance of the y-values of the matching cases. Then, imputation will be done only if

$$\frac{s_m^2}{s_y^2} < v , \tag{B.2}$$

   where s_y^2 is the total variance of y estimated from all complete data on y, and v is the value VR specified on the MI command. This may be interpreted to mean that the matching cases predict the missing value with a reliability of at least $1 - v$. The default value of VR is VR=.5, *i.e.*, $v = .5$. Larger values than this are not recommended. Smaller values may be used if one requires high precision in the imputation. For each value imputed, PRELIS 2 gives the value of the variance ratio and the number of cases on which s_m^2 is based.

If condition (B.2) is satisfied, then y_a is replaced with the mean $\bar{y}_m$ if y is continuous or censored, or with the value on the scale of y closest to $\bar{y}_m$ if y is ordinal. Otherwise, no imputation is done and y_a is left as a missing value.

4. This procedure is repeated for the next case a for which y_a is missing, and so on, until all possible missing values on y have been imputed.

This procedure has the advantage that it gives the same results under linear transformation of the matching variables. Thus, if age is a matching variable, age can be in years or months, or represented by the year of birth, and the resulting imputed data will be the same in each case. Another advantage is that the results of the imputation will be the same regardless of the order of cases in the data.

If *Ivarlist* contains several variables, they will be imputed in the order they are listed. This is of no consequence if no variables in *Ivarlist* is included in *Mvarlist*. Ideally, *Ivarlist* contains the variables with missing values and *Mvarlist* contains variables without missing values. However, PRELIS 2 can handle also the case when some variables are included in both *varlists* and, in fact, the two *varlists* could be identical. If a variable is included in both *varlists*, it is automatically excluded from *Mvarlist* when its values are imputed. In this case, the order of the variables in *Ivarlist* can make a difference, since a variable already imputed can be used as matching variable when another variable is imputed.

Imputation of missing values should be done with utmost care and control, since missing values will be replaced by other values that will be treated as real observed values. If possible, use matching variables which are *not* to be used in the LISREL modeling. Otherwise, if the matching variables are included in the LISREL model, it is likely that the imputation will affect the result of analysis. This should be checked by comparing with the result obtained without imputation.

For each variable to be imputed, PRELIS 2 lists all the cases with missing values. If imputation is successful, it gives the value imputed, the number of matching cases and the variance ratio. If the imputation is not successful, it gives the reason for the failure. This can be either that no matching case was found or that the variance ratio was too large. The XN option on the IM command will make PRELIS 2 list only successful imputations, and the XL option makes PRELIS 2 skip the entire listing of cases. PRELIS 2 always gives the number of missing values per variable, both before and after imputation.

Important note: Imputation is done after all recodings and other data transformations (see the section *Order of computations*, p. 164). If it is required to do recodings or other transformation on the imputed data, one can do this by running PRELIS 2 twice. In the first run, do the imputation and save the raw data (see the section *Saving the raw data*, p. 159). In the second run, use the saved raw data after imputation and do the recodings or other transformations.

Example 7D: Imputation

The following input file (EX7D.PR2) reads the same data as in Example 7B. The missing values on each variable are imputed using all the other variables as matching variables. Cases with missing values are eliminated after imputation. Category labels are then assigned to the data values that remain after listwise deletion and the data screening is done on this subsample.

```
EXAMPLE 7D
Imputing Missing Values
DA NI=6 MI=8,9
LA;NOSAY VOTING COMPLEX NOCARE TOUCH INTEREST
RA FI=EX7.RAW FO;(141X,6F2.0)
IM (NOSAY - INTEREST) (NOSAY - INTEREST)
CL  NOSAY - INTEREST 1=AS 2=A 3=D 4=DS
OU
```

The output file gives the following information concerning missing values and imputation.

```
Number of Missing Values per Variable

      NOSAY    VOTING   COMPLEX    NOCARE    TOUCH   INTEREST
          5         8         3         7       14       14

Imputations for    NOSAY
Case    56 not imputed because of missing values for matching variables
Case    88 imputed  with value      3 (Variance Ratio = .393), NM=    4
Case    99 not imputed because of missing values for matching variables
Case   229 not imputed because of missing values for matching variables
```

Case 274 imputed with value   3 (Variance Ratio = .315), NM=   11

Imputations for   VOTING
Case   13 not imputed because of Variance Ratio = 2.312 (NM=   6)
Case   18 not imputed because of missing values for matching variables
Case   62 not imputed because of missing values for matching variables
Case   99 not imputed because of missing values for matching variables
Case 138 imputed with value   1 (Variance Ratio = .000), NM=   1
Case 180 not imputed because of missing values for matching variables
Case 188 not imputed because of missing values for matching variables
Case 257 imputed with value   2 (Variance Ratio = .324), NM=   13

Imputations for COMPLEX
Case 143 not imputed because of missing values for matching variables
Case 188 not imputed because of missing values for matching variables
Case 240 imputed with value   2 (Variance Ratio = .394), NM=   18

Imputations for   NOCARE
Case   40 not imputed because of missing values for matching variables
Case 143 not imputed because of missing values for matching variables
Case 144 imputed with value   3 (Variance Ratio = .000), NM=   1
Case 206 not imputed because of missing values for matching variables
Case 229 not imputed because of missing values for matching variables
Case 233 imputed with value   3 (Variance Ratio = .000), NM=   1
Case 270 imputed with value   3 (Variance Ratio = .000), NM=   7

Imputations for   TOUCH
Case   18 not imputed because of missing values for matching variables
Case   28 not imputed because of missing values for matching variables
Case   29 imputed with value   2 (Variance Ratio = .000), NM=   1
Case   37 imputed with value   2 (Variance Ratio = .000), NM=   2
Case   40 not imputed because of missing values for matching variables
Case   56 not imputed because of missing values for matching variables
Case   62 not imputed because of missing values for matching variables
Case   99 not imputed because of missing values for matching variables
Case 104 imputed with value   2 (Variance Ratio = .000), NM=   1
Case 143 not imputed because of missing values for matching variables
Case 188 not imputed because of missing values for matching variables
Case 203 not imputed because of missing values for matching variables
Case 209 not imputed because of Variance Ratio = .618 (NM=   5)
Case 238 imputed with value   1 (Variance Ratio = .000), NM=   1

Imputations for INTEREST
Case   12 not imputed because of Variance Ratio = .611 (NM=   3)
Case   18 not imputed because of missing values for matching variables
Case   28 not imputed because of missing values for matching variables
Case   48 imputed with value   2 (Variance Ratio = .000), NM=   2
Case   56 not imputed because of missing values for matching variables
Case   62 not imputed because of missing values for matching variables
Case   64 imputed with value   3 (Variance Ratio = .000), NM=   1
Case   67 imputed with value   2 (Variance Ratio = .000), NM=   1
Case   99 not imputed because of missing values for matching variables
Case 180 not imputed because of missing values for matching variables

```
Case  188 not imputed because of missing values for matching variables
Case  203 not imputed because of missing values for matching variables
Case  206 not imputed because of missing values for matching variables
Case  229 not imputed because of missing values for matching variables
```

```
Number of Missing Values per Variable After Imputation

    NOSAY   VOTING   COMPLEX   NOCARE   TOUCH   INTEREST
      3        6        2         4       10       11

Distribution of Missing Values

Total Sample Size =    312

Number of Missing Values      0     1     2     3     4
       Number of Cases      297     3     5     5     2
Listwise Deletion

Total Effective Sample Size =    297
```

Fifteen data values were successfully imputed, two in NOSAY, two in VOT-
ING, one in COMPLEX, three in NOCARE, four in TOUCH, and three in IN-
TEREST. The listwise sample was increased from 282 to 297. Many cases
could not be imputed because of missing values in the matching variables.
Only three cases could not be imputed because of a variance ratio being
too large. For more successful examples of imputation, see Jöreskog &
Aish (1996).

B.11 Simplified syntax for reading and saving matrices

In PRELIS 1, SM=*filename* on the OU command is used to save the estimated covariance or correlation matrix in a file. In PRELIS 2, one can also
use any of the moment matrix names instead of SM to specify the filename
to be used. Thus, one may use AM, CM, KM, MM, OM, PM, RM, or TM. This
extension has been made to obtain analogy with LISREL 8, where the LIS-
REL 7 command PM FI=*filename* may be simplified to PM=*filename*. Similarly, in LISREL 8, one can write CM=*filename*, KM=*filename*, RM=*filename*,
TM=*filename*,OM= *filename*, etc. Furthermore, one can write AC=*filename* in PRELIS 2 instead of SA=*filename*, and AC=*filename* in LISREL 8
instead of AC FI=*filename*. Also, in PRELIS 2 one can use the simplified
syntax *XX*=*filename* instead of *XX* FI=*filename*, where *XX* may be RA, LA, or
FT (for FT, see the section *Thresholds*, p. 176).

B.12 Saving the raw data

Suppose, the raw data contains many cases and very many variables written in a complicated format with lots of redundant spaces and digits. The file containing the raw data is very large and it takes a long time to read it each time. Suppose, we wish to save the raw data on a small subset of the variables (and possibly also for a subset of the cases) in a compact form for future use and documentation. This can be done by reading the subset of variables by format or SD commands and saving the new raw data by putting SR=*filename* on the OU command. Instead of SR=*filename*, one can write RA=*filename* and the format of the new data file can be specified by WI=*width-of-format* and ND=*number-of-decimals*. For example, if the data on the selected variables are single-digit positive numbers, as is often the case, WI=1 ND=0, will save the data in one-column fields. This will save a lot of space and in future PRELIS runs, the data can be read much faster by the format (*n*F1.0). Note that PRELIS 2 can write data in this form, whereas in FORTRAN this format can only be used to read data, not to write data.

Example 7E: Saving the raw data for a subset of variables and cases

The following input file (EX7E.PR2) saves the raw data on the six variables after imputation, recoding, and listwise deletion. The variables are recoded so they measure Efficacy from low to high. The new raw data is saved in the file EFFICACY.RAW in the format (6F1.0).

```
EXAMPLE 7E
Saving the Raw Data after Imputation, Recoding, and Listwise Deletion
DA NI=6 MI=8,9
LA;NOSAY VOTING COMPLEX NOCARE TOUCH INTEREST
RA FI=EX7.RAW FO;(141X,6F2.0)
IM (NOSAY - INTEREST) (NOSAY - INTEREST)
RE NOSAY - INTEREST OLD=1,2,3,4 NEW=4,3,2,1
CL NOSAY - INTEREST 1=DS 2=D 3=A 4=AS
OU RA=EFFICACY.RAW WI=1 ND=0
```

The file EFFICACY.RAW has 297 lines of 6 columns and contains the complete data on the six variables for further study.

B.13 New variables

Let $x_1, x_2, \ldots, x_k$ denote a set of variables whose labels have been defined. A new variable y can be defined as a function of already defined variables $x_1, x_2, \ldots, x_k$. The general functional form is

$$y = \sum_i a_i \prod_{j=1}^{k} x_j^{b_j} \, ,$$

where a_i is any positive or negative constant and b_j is any constant including zero. Note that $b_j = 0$ means that y does not depend on x_j. If $b_j = 1$, it may be omitted.

New variables can be defined by the following line

NE vary = *some function of old variables*

where vary defines the label for the new variable. If vary is an already existing label, the new variable replaces the old. A separate NE command is used to define each new variable.

The formula defining the new variable is written in a straightforward way. Multiplication is specified by * and exponentiation by ** or ^. Parentheses are not permitted, but this is no restriction because new variables can be functions of other new variables already defined. Division is not permitted, although exponents may be negative. Constants are written as usual. If they are written without a decimal point, they are taken to be integers.

The new variables will be computed for each case in the data. If any of the variables $x_1, x_2, \ldots, x_k$ defining the new variable is missing for a case, the value of the new variable will be missing for this case.

Examples:

```
NE var5=2.5*var1+var2-var3
NE var4=var4-var2
NE var6=var1**2
NE var7=var1*var2
NE var8=var1+var2*var3-var2**2
NE var8=var8**2
```

The last two commands illustrate how one can define var8 as the square of a quadratic expression.

New variables can also be transformed by power or log transformations or recoded. For example, if x is a defined variable, one may define two new variables $y_1 = \sqrt{1 + x^2}$ and $y_2 = \log{(1 + x^2)}$ with the commands:

```
NE  Y1=1+X**2
NE  Y2=1+X**2
PO  Y1 GA=.5
LO  Y2
```

Example 7F: Computing scale scores or factor scores

Suppose, a factor analysis of the six variables NOSAY, VOTING, COM-PLEX, NOCARE, TOUCH, and INTEREST has confirmed that there are two factors, Efficacy and Responsiveness, that NOSAY, VOTING, and COMPLEX are valid indicators of Efficacy, and that NOCARE, TOUCH, and INTEREST are valid indicators of Responsiveness (see Aish & Jö-reskog, 1990). We want to compute scale scores for Efficacy and Respon-siveness defined as the sum of their respective indicators and we want to compute the correlation between these scale scores and the original vari-ables as well as the correlation between the two scale scores. Alternatively, one may want to compute factor scores defined as linear combinations of the observed variables with coefficients obtained as the factor scores regres-sion coefficients estimated by LISREL[3] (see Jöreskog & Sörbom, 1989, p. 93).

To obtain the required scores, add two new variables Efficacy and Respons to the six original variables. The keyword NI specified on the DA command will be increased by one for each NE command defining a *new* label so that the new variables will automatically be included in the analysis. Then, the input file (EX7F.PR2) is as follows:

---

[3]Better factor scores and latent variable scores are available with PRELIS 2.30, see Chapter 3 of Jöreskog *et al.* (1999)

```
! EXAMPLE 7F: Computing Scale Scores
DA NI=6
LA; NOSAY VOTING COMPLEX NOCARE TOUCH INTEREST
RA=EFFICACY.RAW FO; (6F1.0)
NEW EFFICACY = NOSAY + VOTING + COMPLEX
NEW RESPONS = NOCARE + TOUCH + INTEREST
OU MA=PM WP
```

The resulting correlation matrix is of order 8×8:

	NOSAY	VOTING	COMPLEX	NOCARE	TOUCH	INTEREST	EFFICACY	
RESPONS								
NOSAY	1.000							
VOTING	.326	1.000						
COMPLEX	.242	.289	1.000					
NOCARE	.441	.268	.440	1.000				
TOUCH	.337	.167	.315	.663	1.000			
INTEREST	.399	.223	.368	.711	.630	1.000		
EFFICACY	.749	.791	.757	.512	.361	.440	1.000	
RESPONS	.442	.241	.415	.929	.888	.910	.490	1.000

The last two rows of the correlation matrix give the correlations between the scale scores and the original variables, as well as the correlation between the scale scores themselves. Since no variables are declared continuous in the input file, all variables, including EFFICACY and RESPONS, are treated as ordinal. As a result of the NE commands, EFFICACY and RESPONS will have 10 categories with scores ranging from 3 to 12. Since MA=PM, the matrix of polychoric correlations is computed.

Other possibilities are to use MA=KM and treat all variables as continuous to obtain a matrix of product-moment correlations, or to use MA=PM and declare EFFICACY and RESPONS as continuous variables to obtain a matrix of polychoric, polyserial, and product-moment (Pearson) correlations. We leave it to the reader to estimate different type of correlations and compare them.

B.14 Merging files

It is a common situation in practice when working with survey data that some variables are in one file and some are in another file. In particular, this is common in longitudinal or panel studies, where the data have been recorded in separate files for each occasion. In these situations, it is useful to be able to combine some variables from each file and store them in one file for further study.

Suppose that files fname1, fname2, ... contain different sets of variables, all measured on the same cases. To read the variables from different files, use the following type of DA and RA commands:

```
DA NI=n1,n2,...
RA=fname1,fname2,...
```

where n1,n2,... are the number of variables to read from the respective files. As with data from a single file, if no format is given in the input file or the data files, the variables will be read in free format. To read formatted data, put the format first in each data file or put the formats for each data file one after another after the RA command in the input file (in that case the FO option should be given on the RA command).

Example 8: Merging files

The files PANUSA1.RAW and PANUSA2.RAW contain the six Efficacy items from the longitudinal political action survey for the USA (see Aish & Jöreskog, 1990). The first file contains the data collected at the first occasion and the second file contains the data collected at the second occasion. Both files contain data on 933 cases. The following input file (EX8.PR2) will read the data from both files and store the data on all 12 variables in a new file PANUSA.RAW.

```
EXAMPLE 8: Merging two Files
DA NI=6,6
LA
NOSAY1 VOTING1 COMPLEX1 NOCARE1 TOUCH1 INTERES1
NOSAY2 VOTING2 COMPLEX2 NOCARE2 TOUCH2 INTERES2
RA=PANUSA1.RAW,PANUSA2.RAW FO
(6F1.0)
(6F1.0)
OU RA=PANUSA.RAW WI=1 ND=0
```

Note that two formats must follow the FO option on the RA command, and each must begin on a new line.

B.15 Order of computations

In order to understand the performance and results of PRELIS 2, it is essential to be aware of the order in which PRELIS 2 does its computations. We distinguish between four phases defining the order of computations:

- ❑ Data manipulation
- ❑ Treatment of missing values
- ❑ Bootstrap sampling
- ❑ Statistics computation

Data manipulation

Initially, PRELIS 2 works on a data matrix Z consisting of N cases and K variables. In the data manipulation phase, this is transformed to a data matrix z of n cases and k variables. The number n may be smaller than N because of SC or SD commands, which eliminate cases that satisfy certain conditions. The number k may be smaller than K because of SD commands that delete variables after selection of cases. The number k may be larger than K because new variables have been added with NE commands. The data values in z may differ from those in Z because of RE, PO, and LO commands which alter the data values or because new data values have been defined as functions of old data values as specified by NE commands. **In the data manipulation phase, PRELIS 2 does all operations in the order that they appear in the input file**. This is in contrast to PRELIS 1 where the order of commands in the input file did not matter. All commands RE, LO, PO, NE, SC, SD have immediate effect. This means, for example, that:

- ❑ One can recode variables and then select cases on the recoded values, or one can select cases first and then recode variables for the selected cases.
- ❑ One can recode variables and then do power or log transformation on the recoded values, or one can do power or log transformations first and then recode the transformed values.

□ One can define new variables as functions of other variables and then transform or recode these new variables, or one can do transformations first and then define new variables as functions of the transformed values.

Treatment of missing values

Treatment of missing values is done after all data manipulations. If imputation is requested, this is done first. If TR is default or if TR=LI on the DA command, all cases with missing values remaining after imputation will be eliminated and all further computations will be based on the listwise sample. If TR=PA on the DA command, no deletion of cases will be made in the raw data. See also the section *Statistics computation* (p. 165).

Bootstrap sampling

Bootstrap sampling is done after treatment of missing values (see the section *Bootstrap estimates*, p. 171). Bootstrap sampling can only be done after listwise deletion of cases. The statistics reported in the output file refer to this listwise sample, except for means, variances, covariances, and correlations, which are averaged over all bootstrap samples.

Statistics computation

The statistics computation phase consists of univariate, bivariate, and multivariate tables, statistics, and matrices. These are based on the listwise sample z remaining after the data manipulation step and after treatment of missing values. If TR=PA (pairwise deletion) on the DA command, only some of these statistics can be obtained. In this case, all univariate statistics will be based on all cases present for each variable, and all bivariate statistics will be based on all cases present for each pair of variables. No multivariate statistics will be given.

B.16   Tests of univariate and multivariate normality

For each continuous variable, PRELIS 2 gives tests of zero skewness and zero kurtosis. For all continuous variables jointly, PRELIS 2 gives tests of zero multivariate skewness and zero multivariate kurtosis. These tests have been developed by D'Agostino (1986), Mardia (1970, 1974, 1985), Mardia & Foster (1983) and are summarized in Bollen (1989, pp. 420–425).

For an example of these tests of normality, we reconsider the test score data in Example 3A (page 115). The input file (EX3A.PR2) is:

```
EXAMPLE 3A: TEST SCORE DATA
DA NI=11 NO=90
LA FI=LABELS.EX3;RA FI=DATA.EX3
CO ALL;OU MA=KM
```

The output file gives a histogram for each of the nine variables. It is obvious from these histograms that most of the variables are non-normal. This is confirmed by the statistics and tests of normality given in the output:

Univariate Summary Statistics for Continuous Variables

Variable	Mean	St. Dev.	T-Value	Skewness	Kurtosis	Minimum	Freq.	Maximum	Freq.
V01	21.789	7.856	26.312	-1.117	0.256	0.000	2	30.000	6
V02	14.622	7.048	19.682	-0.173	-0.616	0.000	2	28.000	5
V07	11.489	3.069	35.510	-0.175	2.520	0.000	1	20.000	2
V08	14.478	3.660	37.523	-0.490	2.785	0.000	1	25.000	1
V09	19.122	6.830	26.561	-0.635	0.282	0.000	3	32.000	1
V10	21.622	5.560	36.894	-0.553	0.092	6.000	1	33.000	2
V21	15.022	2.998	47.535	-1.956	3.247	4.000	1	17.000	41
V22	13.122	3.304	37.676	-1.123	0.838	2.000	1	17.000	8
V23	12.578	3.402	35.076	-1.141	0.645	3.000	3	16.000	21
V24	8.611	3.550	23.014	-0.271	-0.599	0.000	1	15.000	2
V25	16.589	4.271	36.844	-1.338	2.280	1.000	1	22.000	9

Test of Univariate Normality for Continuous Variables

	Skewness		Kurtosis		Skewness and Kurtosis	
Variable	Z-Score	P-Value	Z-Score	P-Value	Chi-Square	P-Value
V01	-4.372	0.000	0.812	0.417	19.772	0.000

APPENDIX B: NEW FEATURES IN PRELIS 2

```
V02   -0.679   0.497   -1.376   0.169      2.355   0.308
V07   -0.685   0.493    3.068   0.002      9.880   0.007
V08   -1.917   0.055    3.222   0.001     14.059   0.001
V09   -2.488   0.013    0.855   0.392      6.919   0.031
V10   -2.166   0.030    0.515   0.607      4.958   0.084
V21   -7.659   0.000    3.465   0.001     70.665   0.000
V22   -4.397   0.000    1.644   0.100     22.037   0.000
V23   -4.469   0.000    1.400   0.162     21.933   0.000
V24   -1.062   0.288   -1.314   0.189      2.853   0.240
V25   -5.239   0.000    2.916   0.004     35.946   0.000
```

Relative Multivariate Kurtosis = 1.179

Test of Multivariate Normality for Continuous Variables

	Skewness			Kurtosis			Skewness and Kurtosis	
Value	Z-Score	P-Value	Value	Z-Score	P-Value	Chi-Square	P-Value
42.810	11.130	0.000	28.709	5.216	0.000	151.072	0.000

The tests of multivariate normality are rather time consuming to compute. One can skip this computation by putting XM on the OU command.

B.17 Rank correlations and tau-c correlations

PRELIS can compute many different correlations or measures of associations between ordinal variables. In addition to those available in PRELIS 1, Spearman rank correlations can be obtained for all pairs of ordinal variables by putting MA=RM on the OU command. Similarly, by putting MA=TM, one will obtain Kendall's tau-c correlations.

B.18 Asymptotic covariance matrices

Asymptotic covariance matrices produced by PRELIS 2 differ fundamentally from those produced by PRELIS 1 in two ways:

□ in the way they are stored in files
□ in the way they are computed (estimated)

Storage

PRELIS computes asymptotic covariance (AC) matrices using double precision. In PRELIS 1, the AC matrix was saved in a file in the format (6D13.6) to be read by LISREL. To avoid loosing accuracy in the transfer between PRELIS and LISREL, PRELIS 2 stores the AC matrix on file in *binary form*. This has the advantage that the file is smaller and can be read faster. There is a slight disadvantage, however, because the file containing the AC matrix is no longer readable, that is, one cannot use the DOS command TYPE, the SSI utility DISP, or an editor to look at the file. A utility program BIN2ASC is provided to convert the binary file to ASCII format. If the file *infile* contains an asymptotic covariance matrix in binary form, the DOS command

BIN2ASC *infile outfile*

will convert this asymptotic covariance matrix to ASCII format and store it in the file *outfile*. The ASCII file contains all the elements in the lower half of the asymptotic covariance matrix, including the diagonal, written rowwise in the format (3D23.16). This is intended for users who want to "look at" the elements of the asymptotic covariance matrix or use this matrix in other programs. The ASCII format may also be used to transfer the asymptotic covariance matrix from one computer system to another if it is difficult to transfer the binary file. Most users of PRELIS have no need to use BIN2ASC.

A similar routine ASC2BIN is provided to convert an ASCII file containing an asymptotic covariance matrix to binary form. Thus the DOS command

ASC2BIN *infile outfile*

will convert the ASCII file *infile* to the binary file *outfile*. This is provided for the purpose of converting an ASCII asymptotic covariance matrix back to binary form after transporting it from one system to another, as mentioned above. It may also be used to convert an asymptotic covariance matrix produced by PRELIS 1, so that it can be read by LISREL 8. Note that LISREL 8 can only read an asymptotic covariance matrix in binary form.

Estimation

The estimates of asymptotic variances and covariances of product moment and polychoric correlations have been improved.

Due to an error in the formula, the asymptotic covariance matrix for MA=KM is incorrect in PRELIS 1 (the error was corrected in version 1.14 of PRELIS). The same error also affects the asymptotic covariance matrix for MA=PM if some of the variables are continuous.

For the case of MA=PM and all variables ordinal, the estimation of the asymptotic covariance matrix in PRELIS 1 was based on the simplifying assumption that two different polychoric correlations are asymptotically uncorrelated for given thresholds, an assumption which does not necessarily hold. PRELIS 2 gives a consistent estimate of the asymptotic covariance matrix of polychoric correlations without making this simplifying assumption (see Jöreskog, 1994).

The asymptotic covariance matrix of an augmented moment matrix (MA=AM) can now be obtained. This is needed for simultaneous estimation of some mean and covariance structures.

The differences in AC matrices between PRELIS 1 and PRELIS 2 have fundamental implications for standard errors and chi-square values in LISREL when the LISREL model is estimated by WLS.

Singularity

The asymptotic covariance matrix $\mathbf{W}$ produced by PRELIS 2 is read by LISREL 8. If the LISREL 8 input file requests selection of variables, LISREL 8 will delete some rows and columns of $\mathbf{W}$. In principle, $\mathbf{W}$, after selection of variables, if any, should be positive definite. If it is, LISREL 8 will compute $\mathbf{W}^{-1}$, the weight matrix in the fit function for WLS.

However, there are situations where the asymptotic covariance matrix $\mathbf{W}$ produced by PRELIS 2 may be singular or ill-conditioned (very nearly singular). In such a situation it is better to use a symmetric Moore-Penrose generalized inverse $\mathbf{W}^-$ instead of $\mathbf{W}^{-1}$ as a weight matrix in the fit function for WLS. LISREL 8.30 will automatically use $\mathbf{W}^-$ as a weight matrix if $\mathbf{W}$ is singular.

Some users may want to examine the eigenvalues of $\mathbf{W}$. To do so, put the asymptotic covariance matrix $\mathbf{W}$ produced by PRELIS 2 in the file *infile*.AC, run the utility program GINV with the DOS command line

GINV *infile*.AC *outfile*.WM

where *outfile*.WM is the filename where the weight matrix $\mathbf{W}^-$ is to be stored. Then, in the LISREL 8 input file, use the command line

WM= *outfile*.WM

to read this weight matrix. If a WM command is used, no selection of variables is possible in LISREL 8 since the selection of variables must be done in $\mathbf{W}$ before the generalized inverse is computed. If selection of variables is necessary, they can be done, by using SD commands, for example, in PRELIS 2.

The weight matrix $\mathbf{W}^-$ produced by GINV is stored in binary form in *outfile*.WM. It is obtained by computing all eigenvalues of $\mathbf{W}$ greater than ϵ, k say, and the corresponding eigenvectors and then using the formula

$$\mathbf{W}^- = \mathbf{U}_k \mathbf{D}_k^{-1} \mathbf{U}_k' \ ,$$

where $\mathbf{D}_k$ is a diagonal matrix of the k largest eigenvalues of $\mathbf{W}$ and $\mathbf{U}_k$ is a matrix with the corresponding orthonormal eigenvectors as columns.

In addition to the binary file *outfile*.WM, GINV gives an ordinary output file called OUTPUT which gives all the eigenvalues of $\mathbf{W}$. This can be used to inspect the eigenvalues and to decide on a suitable value of ϵ.

The default value of ϵ is 10^{-12}. Larger values can be used but ϵ should not be chosen too large. To change ϵ, use the following DOS command line to execute GINV:

GINV *infile*.AC *outfile*.WM -EPS= *e*

where *e* is the required value of ϵ.

Sample size restriction

The minimum sample size required for estimating asymptotic covariance matrices is

$$\frac{k(k-1)}{2} \quad \text{for} \quad \text{MA=KM} \quad \text{and} \quad \text{MA=PM}$$

$$\frac{k(k+1)}{2} \quad \text{for} \quad \text{MA=CM}$$

$$\frac{(k+1)(k+2)}{2} \quad \text{for} \quad \text{MA=AM}$$

where k is the number of variables. There is no guarantee that sample sizes as low as these will give good estimates of the asymptotic covariance matrix. Rather, these values are to be regarded as absolute minimum values. For sample sizes below these, the asymptotic covariance matrix will not be positive definite and thus cannot be used in LISREL. The MS keyword in PRELIS 1 is no longer valid.

B.19   Bootstrap estimates

Bootstrap estimates of the matrix specified with MA=*XX* (*XX*=CM, KM, PM, OM, RM, TM, etc.) on the OU command and its asymptotic covariance matrix specified with SA=*filename* or AC=*filename* may be obtained. This is controlled with the following keywords on the OU command:

- BS   number of bootstrap samples to be generated
- SF   sample fraction of each sample in percentage
- IX   integer starting value for the random number generator
- BM   to save all the *MA*-matrices computed for each bootstrap sample to a file
- ME   to save all the mean vectors computed for each bootstrap sample to a file
- SD   to save all the standard deviations computed for each bootstrap sample to a file

If BS=n, the MA-matrix in the output will be the mean of all n bootstrap estimates and the AC-matrix will be the empirical covariance matrix of all n bootstrap estimates. The latter is often a better estimate than that estimated from asymptotic theory. Note that this option makes it possible to estimate the asymptotic covariance matrix for OM, RM, TM matrices that are otherwise not available.

Example 9: Estimating the asymptotic covariance matrix by bootstrap

The file EFFICACY.RAW obtained in Example 7E contains data on six or-dinal variables for 297 cases. The following input file (EX9.PR2) will generate 50 bootstrap samples of 148 cases each and estimate the RM-matrix (Spearman rank correlations) for each of these samples.

All the estimated RM matrices are saved in the file BOOTSTR.RML, their mean is saved in the file EFFICACY.RMB and 141 times their covariance matrix is saved in binary form in the file EFFICACY.ACR.

```
EXAMPLE 9
ESTIMATING RM AND AC MATRICES BY BOOTSTRAP
DA NI=6
LA=EFFICACY.LAB
RA=EFFICACY.RAW FO;(6F1.0)
OU MA=RM BS=50 SF=50 RM=EFFICACY.RMB AC=EFFICACY.ACR BM=BOOTSTR.RML
```

The RM-matrix in EFFICACY.RMB may be analyzed by WLS in LISREL 8 as follows.

```
ESTIMATING MODEL BY ANALYZING AN RM MATRIX BY WLS. THE RM MATRIX AND
THE AC MATRIX HAVE BEEN GENERATED BY BOOTSTRAP IN PRELIS 2
DA NI=6 NO=141 MA=RM
LA=EFFICACY.LAB
RM=EFFICACY.RMB
AC=EFFICACY.ACR
MO ....
....
OU
```

Other aspects of bootstrapping and Monte Carlo experimenting with PRELIS 2 and LISREL 8 are considered in Appendix C.

B.20 Homogeneity tests for categorical variables

Consider two categorical variables with the same number of categories k. The bivariate probability distribution of these variables is represented by the matrix of probabilities

$$
\Pi = \begin{pmatrix}
\pi_{11} & \pi_{12} & \cdots & \pi_{1k} \\
\pi_{21} & \pi_{22} & \cdots & \pi_{2k} \\
\vdots & \vdots & \ddots & \vdots \\
\pi_{k1} & \pi_{k2} & \cdots & \pi_{kk}
\end{pmatrix} ,
$$

where π_{ij} is the probability that the first variable falls in category i and the second variable falls in category j.

The homogeneity test is a test of the hypothesis that the two marginal distributions are the same:

$$
\sum_{j=1}^{k} \pi_{ij} = \sum_{j=1}^{k} \pi_{ji} .
$$

Let

$$
\mathbf{P} = \begin{pmatrix}
p_{11} & p_{12} & \cdots & p_{1k} \\
p_{21} & p_{22} & \cdots & p_{2k} \\
\vdots & \vdots & \ddots & \vdots \\
p_{k1} & p_{k2} & \cdots & p_{kk}
\end{pmatrix} .
$$

be the corresponding sample proportions and let $d_i = \sum_{j=1}^{k}(p_{ij} - p_{ji})$, $i = 1, 2, \ldots, k - 1$. Then the Wald statistic for testing this hypothesis is $\mathbf{d}'\mathbf{A}^{-1}\mathbf{d}$, where $\mathbf{d}$ is a vector of order $k-1$ with elements $d_1, d_2, \ldots, d_{k-1}$, and $\mathbf{A}$ is the covariance matrix of $\mathbf{d}$. $\mathbf{A}$ is readily determined from the fact that (Agresti, 1990, eq. 12.5)

$$
N\mathrm{Cov}(p_{gh}, p_{ij}) = \delta_{gi}\delta_{hj}\pi_{gh}\pi_{ij} - \pi_{gh}\pi_{ij} ,
$$

where

$$
\delta_{ij} = \left\{ \begin{array}{ll} 0 \text{ if } & i \neq j \\ 1 \text{ if } & i = j \end{array} \right\} .
$$

If the hypothesis of homogeneity holds, this statistic is distributed as χ^2 with $k - 1$ degrees of freedom.

The homogeneity test is particularly useful in two-wave longitudinal studies to test the hypothesis that the distribution of a variable has not changed from the first occasion to the second.

To test homogeneity with PRELIS 2 include the command

HT *varlist*

in the input file. PRELIS 2 tests the homogeneity pairwise for every pair of variables in *varlist*. Note that this test can be applied to nominal as well as ordinal variables.

For ordinal variables, the homogeneity test (HT*test*) described here is different from the equal thresholds test (ET*test*) described in the section *Thresholds* (p. 176) in two ways:

❏ It does not assume underlying normal variables.
❏ If underlying normality is assumed, the homogeneity hypothesis implies the equal thresholds hypothesis.

Example 10A: Testing homogeneity in panel data

Aish & Jöreskog (1990) analyze data on political attitudes. Their data consists of six ordinal variables measured on the same people at two occasions. The six variables are considered to be indicators of Political Efficacy and System Responsiveness. The following input file (EX10A.PR2) will read the 12 variables (six variables at two occasions) for every odd-numbered case and test the hypothesis that the univariate marginal distribution is stable over time for each of the six variables. (The data file PANUSA.RAW was generated in Example 8.)

```
EXAMPLE 10A
TESTING HOMOGENEITY FOR EACH VARIABLE OVER TIME
POLITICAL ACTION PANEL DATA FOR USA
DA NI=12 MI=8,9
LA
NOSAY1 VOTING1 COMPLEX1 NOCARE1 TOUCH1 INTERES1
NOSAY2 VOTING2 COMPLEX2 NOCARE2 TOUCH2 INTERES2
RA=PANUSA.RAW FO;(12F1.0)
```

```
SC  CASE=ODD                      !This selects every odd-numbered case
CL  ALL  1=AS  2=A  3=D  4=DS
HT  NOSAY1  NOSAY2
HT  VOTING1  VOTING2
HT  COMPLEX1  COMPLEX2
HT  NOCARE1  NOCARE2
HT  TOUCH1  TOUCH2
HT  INTERES1  INTERES2
OU  MA=TM
```

Some matrix must be specified on the OU command to make the program compute all the bivariate marginal contingency tables that are needed for the calculation of the test statistics. Any matrix appropriate for ordinal variables will do, that is, OM, PM, RM, or TM. Here we use MA=TM.

With ordinal variables, PRELIS 2 gives a bivariate contingency table for each pair of variables, both in absolute frequencies and in percentages. With 12 variables, as in this example, there will be 66 such tables of each kind. One can put the XB option on the OU command to skip the printing of these tables in the output file.

The output file reveals the following results for the homogeneity tests:

Homogeneity Tests

Variable	vs.	Variable	Chi-Squ.	D.F.	P-Value
NOSAY1	vs.	NOSAY2	4.737	3	0.192
VOTING1	vs.	VOTING2	2.494	3	0.476
COMPLEX1	vs.	COMPLEX2	8.767	3	0.033
NOCARE1	vs.	NOCARE2	4.377	3	0.223
TOUCH1	vs.	TOUCH2	8.087	3	0.044
INTERES1	vs.	INTERES2	4.450	3	0.217

None of the tests are significant at the one percent level, whereas the tests for COMPLEX and TOUCH are significant at the five percent level. Thus, it appears that the marginal distributions are not changing much over time. The amount of change can be seen more clearly in the corresponding bivariate contingency tables given in the output file. For example, for NOSAY we have

		NOSAY2		
NOSAY1	AS	A	D	DS
AS	8	11	13	1
A	4	59	42	3
D	8	37	170	20
DS	0	4	19	10

or in percentages

```
              NOSAY2
NOSAY1   AS    A     D    DS
  AS    2.0   2.7   3.2   .2
   A    1.0  14.4  10.3   .7
   D    2.0   9.0  41.6  4.9
  DS     .0   1.0   4.6  2.4
```

B.21 Thresholds

PRELIS computes threshold estimates for ordinal variables. PRELIS 1 did not give these in the output file, but PRELIS 2 will always print them whenever they are computed.

The command

ET *varlist*

will make PRELIS 2 estimate the thresholds under the condition that they are *equal* for all ordinal variables in *varlist* (see Jöreskog, 1990). A test of equal thresholds can be obtained by running PRELIS 2 with and without the ET command and computing the difference in chi-squares for each polychoric correlation. This is useful in panel studies when the variables in *varlist* represent the same ordinal variable measured at different occasions. PRELIS 2 will then estimate the means and the variances of the variables underlying the ordinal variables relative to a common scale for all the variables in *varlist*. The origin and unit of measurement of this common scale is fixed so that the sum of the means is zero and the sum of the variances equals the number of variables in *varlist*. Similarly, by pooling data from several groups, one can estimate the thresholds to be the same over groups. These common thresholds can be saved in a file by writing TH=*filename* on the OU command. Polychoric correlations and means and variances of the variables underlying the ordinal variables can then be estimated for each group separately by including the commands:

FT = *filename varlist1*
FT *varlist2*
FT *varlist3*
· · ·
· · ·

and reading the fixed thresholds from the file *filename*. The first line in this file contains the thresholds that will be assigned to the variables in *varlist1*. The thresholds in the second line in the file will be assigned to the variables in *varlist2*, etc. In most applications, each *varlist* will contain only one variable.

Example :

```
FT=THRESH X2 X4 X5
FT X1 X3
```

will set the thresholds equal for variables X2, X4, and X5 and read the values for these thresholds from the first line in the file THRESH, and then set the thresholds equal for variables X1 and X3 and read the values for these thresholds from the second line in the file THRESH.

Example 10B: Panel data for political efficacy

Consider the same data as in Example 10A. The following input file (EX10B.PR2) will analyze the 12 variables (six variables at two occasions) and estimate the covariance matrix and the corresponding asymptotic covariance matrix under the condition that the thresholds are equal over time for each of the six variables.

```
! EXAMPLE 10B
! COMPUTING POLYCHORIC CORRELATION MATRIX AND ASYMPTOTIC COVARIANCE
! MATRIX UNDER EQUAL THRESHOLDS FOR EACH VARIABLE OVER TIME
! POLITICAL ACTION PANEL DATA FOR USA
DA NI=12 MI=8,9
LA
NOSAY1 VOTING1 COMPLEX1 NOCARE1 TOUCH1 INTERES1
NOSAY2 VOTING2 COMPLEX2 NOCARE2 TOUCH2 INTERES2
RA=PANUSA.RAW FO;(12F1.0)
SC CASE=ODD
CL ALL 1=AS 2=A 3=D 4=DS
ET NOSAY1 NOSAY2;   ET VOTING1 VOTING2; ET COMPLEX1 COMPLEX2
ET NOCARE1 NOCARE2; ET TOUCH1 TOUCH2;   ET INTERES1 INTERES2
OU MA=CM CM=PANELUSA.CML AC=PANELUSA.ACC
```

Note that:

- The missing values are defined as 8 and 9 on the DA command
- Category labels are defined for all variables on the CL command
- The six ET commands specify that the thresholds are to be equal for each variable over time.
- On the OU command,

    - MA=CM means that the covariance matrix should be computed,
    - CM=PANELUSA.CML means that the covariance matrix should be saved in the file PANELUSA.CML,
    - AC=PANELUSA.ACC means that the asymptotic covariance matrix should be saved in the file PANELUSA.ACC.

Since all variables are ordinal, the covariance matrix has a special meaning. In PRELIS 1, this was the covariance matrix of the normal scores of the ordinal variables, but in PRELIS 2 it is a scaled polychoric correlation matrix. PRELIS 2 first estimates the polychoric correlations and the means and standard deviations under equal thresholds and then scales the correlation matrix to a covariance matrix using the estimated standard deviations. This kind of covariance matrix is useful not only in longitudinal studies with ordinal variables, but also in multigroup studies with ordinal variables. See Jöreskog & Aish (1996) for further examples. Formulas will be given in Jöreskog & Sörbom (1996).

B.22 Multivariate multinomial probit regressions

A major new feature in PRELIS 2 is the distinction between y- and x-variables. The x-variables can be fixed or random variables. If they are random, their joint distribution is unspecified and assumed not to contain any parameters of interest. These x-variables can be dummy-coded categorical variables or measured variables on an interval scale assumed not to contain measurement error. As before, the y-variables can be continuous, censored, or ordinal variables. Most of the analysis that is done by PRELIS 2 is concerned with the conditional distribution of y for given x, but PRELIS 2 will also estimate the unconditional joint covariance matrix of y and x and its asymptotic covariance matrix. These can be used with WLS in LISREL 8 in an analysis with fixed-x.

PRELIS 1 did not make the distinction between y- and x-variables, *i.e.*, all variables were assumed to be y-variables. PRELIS 2 assumes by default that all variables are y-variables. To specify x-variables, include a command

FI *varlist*

in the input file, where *varlist* is a list of the x-variables. All variables not listed in *varlist* are assumed to be y-variables. All y-variables are assumed to be ordinal, unless they are declared continuous or censored.

For each ordinal y-variable, PRELIS 2 will estimate the univariate probit regression of y^* on the x-variables, where y^* is the variable underlying y. For each pair of ordinal variables, PRELIS 2 will also estimate conditional polychoric correlation for given x. Jöreskog & Aish (1996) give further details and several applications of structural equation modeling with ordinal and fixed variables.

There are three different ways of handling the thresholds in the probit regressions:

- ❑ The thresholds may be estimated jointly with the regression coefficients in the probit regressions. This is the default alternative.
- ❑ The thresholds may be estimated from the marginal distributions of the ordinal variables. The regression coefficients in the probit regressions are then estimated for fixed thresholds. To specify this alternative, include a command
  MT *varlist*
  in the input file.
- ❑ The regression coefficients in the probit regressions may be estimated for fixed thresholds specified by the user. To specify this alternative, include a command
  FT = *filename varlist*
  in the input file.

In the second and third alternative, *varlist* may be ALL to specify that this should be done for all ordinal variables. Note that, if *varlist* contains only a subset of the ordinal variables, one can have mixtures of any two or all three alternatives.

Example 11: Fixed-x and probit regression

The following input file (EX11.PR2) reads data on two ordinal variables and two fixed variables and estimates the probit regressions of each ordinal variable on the x-variables and the conditional polychoric correlation between the two ordinal variables. The joint covariance matrix of the four variables and the corresponding asymptotic covariance matrix is also estimated.

```
EXAMPLE 11: TEST OF FIXED-X
DA NI=4
RA=EX11.RAW
FI 3 4
OU MA=CM AC=DATA.ACC PA
```

The output file gives the following results.

```
Univariate Probit Regression for    VAR 1

THRESHOLDS: -1.433   -0.330   0.393
            (0.177)  (0.138) (0.137)

   VAR 1 = 0.919*VAR 3 + 1.757*VAR 4 + Error, R  = 0.968
       (0.0939)         (0.157)
        9.788           11.171
```

$$\text{VAR 1} = 0.919 \cdot \text{VAR 3} + 1.757 \cdot \text{VAR 4} + \text{Error}, \quad R^2 = 0.968$$

```
Univariate Probit Regression for    VAR 2

THRESHOLDS: -0.532    0.297    1.234
            (0.0766) (0.0752) (0.0933)

   VAR 2 = 0.480*VAR 3 + 0.0959*VAR 4 + Error, R  = 0.564
       (0.0355)        (0.0255)
        13.512          3.766
```

$$\text{VAR 2} = 0.480 \cdot \text{VAR 3} + 0.0959 \cdot \text{VAR 4} + \text{Error}, \quad R^2 = 0.564$$

Conditional Correlation Matrix

	VAR 1	VAR 2
VAR 1	1.000	
VAR 2	0.630 (0.074) 8.481	1.000

Covariance Matrix

	VAR 1	VAR 2	VAR 3	VAR 4
VAR 1	31.217			
VAR 2	5.685	2.296		
VAR 3	7.918	2.371	4.508	
VAR 4	13.057	1.637	2.148	6.308

Means

VAR 1	VAR 2	VAR 3	VAR 4
0.653	0.151	0.269	0.231

Standard Deviations

VAR 1	VAR 2	VAR 3	VAR 4
5.587	1.515	2.123	2.512

Asymptotic Covariance Matrix of Variances and Covariances

	S(1,1)	S(2,1)	S(2,2)	S(3,1)	S(3,2)	S(3,3)
S(1,1)	4.11224					
S(2,1)	0.71651	0.21083				
S(2,2)	0.11296	0.05099	0.02419			
S(3,1)	1.14192	0.26379	0.04663	0.48278		
S(3,2)	0.19164	0.05831	0.01931	0.09452	0.02863	
S(3,3)	0.28865	0.07746	0.01687	0.15240	0.03811	0.06862
S(4,1)	1.74233	0.25689	0.03251	0.40624	0.06092	0.08842
S(4,2)	0.31445	0.08393	0.01427	0.10569	0.01839	0.02650
S(4,3)	0.49661	0.10755	0.01577	0.19254	0.03218	0.05089
S(4,4)	0.72494	0.08723	0.00971	0.13138	0.01854	0.02384

Asymptotic Covariance Matrix of Variances and Covariances

	S(4,1)	S(4,2)	S(4,3)	S(4,4)
S(4,1)	0.79070			
S(4,2)	0.12329	0.03907		
S(4,3)	0.18586	0.04701	0.08310	
S(4,4)	0.35102	0.04443	0.06215	0.16728

Each univariate probit regression is given in equation form with standard errors in parentheses below the regression coefficients and t-values below the standard errors. Standard errors and t-values are also given for the conditional polychoric correlations. Standard errors (without t-values) are given for the threshold estimates.

C | Simulation with PRELIS 2 and LISREL 8

C.1 Introduction

By simulation we mean here drawing random samples of data from some population, estimating various parameters from each sample for the purpose of studying the mean and variance and other characteristics of the distribution of these parameter estimates. There are two techniques for drawing the random samples: bootstrap and Monte Carlo. In bootstrapping the random samples are drawn from an original sample, which usually is a sample of empirical data but which can also be a set of artificial data. In Monte Carlo sampling, the samples are generated from randomly generated variables so no real data is involved. Various combinations of the two techniques are also possible.

This appendix illustrates how bootstrapping and Monte Carlo experimenting can be done with PRELIS 2 and LISREL 8. We emphasize the interplay between the two programs. Typically, the random samples are generated by PRELIS. These samples are then analyzed by LISREL. The sampling distribution of the parameter estimates or other quantities produced by LISREL are then studied by PRELIS.

The quantities which distributions can be studied in this way are parameter estimates, goodness-of-fit-statistics, fitted variances, covariances or correlations, factor scores regressions, and estimated asymptotic covariance matrices of parameter estimators (anything that can be saved in files, see p. 73 of Jöreskog & Sörbom, 1989) and these can be studied under any combination of *type of matrix analyzed* (MA = AM, CM, KM,

MM, OM, PM, RM, TM) and *method of estimation* (ME = IV, TSLS, ULS, GLS, ML, WLS, DWLS). The vector of estimated free parameters can be saved by putting PV=*filename1* and the vector of corresponding standard errors can be saved by putting SV=*filename2* on the OU command. The t-values may be saved by putting TV=*filename3* on the OU command.

We illustrate these procedures on several examples in such a way that anybody interested can carry out these experiments directly and use any variation of them as required. The data file for the bootstrap example is EFFICACY.RAW and the input files are BS.ST1 – BS.ST3. For the Monte Carlo experiments the input files are denoted SIMEX*ij.XXX*, where *i* is the example number, *j* is a sequence number within example, and *XXX* is PR2 for a PRELIS 2 input file and LS8 for a LISREL 8 input file. To avoid excessive output files in simulations, put XO or XO=0 on the OU command.

For both bootstrapping and Monte Carlo experimenting, we use the random number generator of Schrage (1979) to generate uniform random numbers in double precision. This requires a seed as a starting number for the generator. The seed may be specified as IX=i on the OU command of the PRELIS input file, where i is a random integer. If IX is not specified, its value will be set equal to the number of seconds passed since last midnight. In this case, this means that if two persons run the same input file or if one person runs the same input file at different occasions, the two runs will not produce the same result, although the two results represent realizations of the same random phenomenon. To reproduce exactly the same result as reported here, one must use the same seed as we have used.

C.2 Bootstrapping

The original data consists of N cases and we want to draw K samples of size n. The drawing is done with replacement. The number n may be smaller than, equal to, or larger than N. For each of the K samples, some statistics are computed and saved in a file. We assume here that the data matrix of order $N \times k$ does not contain missing values. (If it does, just specify the missing values in the input file in Step 1, see Appendix B; all bootstrap samples will be drawn from the listwise sample remaining after deletion of all cases with missing values.)

Bootstrap example

Suppose, we want to study the distribution of the factor loadings (some of them or all of them) in LISREL when a specified model is estimated by ML on the basis of a matrix of Kendall's tau-c correlations. There is no statistical theory that justifies using ML to fit a model to a matrix of tau-c correlations. In particular, one cannot rely on standard errors of parameter estimates. However, with the bootstrap technique one can estimate valid standard errors in this case.

To illustrate, we draw 100 bootstrap samples of size 148 from the raw data in file EFFICACY.RAW containing 297 cases on six variables (see Appendix B, Example 7E).

Step 1

Run PRELIS 2 with the following input file (BS.ST1):

```
! Generating 100 TM matrices (Kendall's tau-c correlations)
! by bootstrapping from EFFICACY.RAW
DA NI=6
LA=EFFICACY.LAB; RA=EFFICACY.RAW FO; (6F1.0)
OU MA=TM BS=100 SF=50 BM=EFFICACY.TMB IX=1234567
```

Here, BS=100 is the number of bootstrap samples to be drawn and SF is the sample fraction as a percentage: With SF=50, each bootstrap sample will be of size 148.

After this run, the file EFFICACY.TMB contains 100 matrices of tau-c correlations. The correlation matrices for the first two bootstrap samples are:

```
0.10000D+01   0.20465D+00   0.10000D+01   0.16874D+00   0.13063D+00   0.10000D+01
0.34015D+00   0.37071D+00   0.16910D+00   0.10000D+01   0.29981D+00   0.14929D+00
0.13902D+00   0.49703D+00   0.10000D+01   0.27222D+00   0.28719D+00   0.12540D+00
0.54468D+00   0.45403D+00   0.10000D+01
```

```
0.10000D+01  0.15096D+00  0.10000D+01  0.14767D+00  0.14232D+00  0.10000D+01
0.25128D+00  0.37497D-01  0.24069D+00  0.10000D+01  0.17385D+00 -0.40297D-01
0.20441D+00  0.44375D+00  0.10000D+01  0.24617D+00  0.69394D-02  0.17994D+00
0.44741D+00  0.40881D+00  0.10000D+01
```

Step 2

Each of the 100 correlation matrices generated in Step 1 will be analyzed by LISREL 8 by fitting a specific two-factor model. The matrix of factor loadings Λ_x (LX) estimated in each sample will be saved in a file EFFI-CACY.LXB. The LISREL 8 input file (BS.ST2) has the following form:

```
! Estimating 100 LX matrices (factor loadings) from EFFICACY.TMB
DA NI=6 NO=148 RP=100
LA=EFFICACY.LAB REWIND
KM=EFFICACY.TMB
MO NX=6 NK=2
FR LX(1,1) LX(2,1) LX(3,1) LX(4,1) LX(4,2) LX(5,2) LX(6,2)
OU LX=EFFICACY.LXB XM
```

The RP=100 means *repeat 100 times* and has the same effect as stacking 100 input files after each other, *i.e.*, the input file above will be read 100 times. Note that the labels file (EFFICACY.LAB) is rewound after each sample has been analyzed. The XM option on the OU command tells LISREL 8 not to compute modification indices. This saves some computer time.

This run will produce a huge output file containing the printed output for each of the 100 analyses. If these results are of no interest, one can avoid this by putting XO or XO=0 on the OU command. XO generates output for the first repetition; XO=0 generates no output file at all.

This step produces the file EFFICACY.LXB containing 100 matrices of factor loadings. The set of factor loadings for the first two bootstrap samples are:

```
0.48248D+00  0.00000D+00  0.47330D+00  0.00000D+00  0.25828D+00  0.00000D+00
0.33406D+00  0.50911D+00  0.00000D+00  0.63967D+00  0.00000D+00  0.70979D+00
0.45935D+00  0.00000D+00  0.16622D+00  0.00000D+00  0.42176D+00  0.00000D+00
0.13412D+00  0.60700D+00  0.00000D+00  0.62942D+00  0.00000D+00  0.64950D+00
```

Step 3

The empirical distribution of the 100 sets of factor loadings in EFFICA-CY.LXB generated in Step 2 can be studied by running PRELIS 2, treating the factor loadings as continuous variables. PRELIS 2 gives the mean, variance, skewness, kurtosis, maximum, and minimum, as well as a histogram for each loading. Univariate and multivariate tests of normality are also given.

The PRELIS 2 input file (BS.ST3) for Step 3 is:

```
! Analyzing 100 LX matrices (factor loadings) in EFFICACY.LXB
DA NI=12
LA
'LX(1,1)' 'LX(1,2)' 'LX(2,1)' 'LX(2,2)' 'LX(3,1)' 'LX(3,2)' 'LX(4,1)'
'LX(4,2)' 'LX(5,1)' 'LX(5,2)' 'LX(6,1)' 'LX(6,2)'
RA=EFFICACY.LXB
CO ALL
SD 'LX(1,2)' 'LX(2,2)' 'LX(3,2)' 'LX(5,1)' 'LX(6,1)'
OU MA=KM WP
```

Since the fixed zero factor loadings are of no interest, we use an SD command to eliminate these. The results are as follows:

Univariate Summary Statistics for Continuous Variables

Variable	Mean	St. Dev.	T-Value	Skewness	Kurtosis	Minimum	Freq.	Maximum	Freq.
LX(1,1)	0.527	0.089	59.022	0.015	-0.106	0.287	1	0.763	1
LX(2,1)	0.395	0.101	38.958	-0.533	0.338	0.079	1	0.592	1
LX(3,1)	0.428	0.077	55.694	-0.454	0.221	0.196	1	0.612	1
LX(4,1)	0.060	0.376	1.584	-0.456	8.429	-1.729	1	1.753	1
LX(4,2)	0.700	0.377	18.564	0.274	9.467	-1.049	1	2.518	1
LX(5,2)	0.589	0.074	79.892	-0.462	-0.341	0.402	1	0.741	1
LX(6,2)	0.661	0.074	89.552	-0.641	0.344	0.429	1	0.806	1

Test of Univariate Normality for Continuous Variables

	Skewness		Kurtosis		Skewness and Kurtosis	
Variable	Z-Score	P-Value	Z-Score	P-Value	Chi-Square	P-Value
LX(1,1)	0.061	0.951	0.079	0.937	0.010	0.995
LX(2,1)	-2.197	0.028	0.964	0.335	5.755	0.056
LX(3,1)	-1.873	0.061	0.758	0.448	4.083	0.130
LX(4,1)	-1.880	0.060	5.168	0.000	30.245	0.000

```
LX(4,2)   1.131   0.258     5.357   0.000      29.972   0.000
LX(5,2)  -1.906   0.057    -0.541   0.588       3.926   0.140
LX(6,2)  -2.644   0.008     0.974   0.330       7.940   0.019
```

Test of Multivariate Normality for Continuous Variables

	Skewness			Kurtosis			Skewness and Kurtosis	
Value	Z-Score	P-Value	Value	Z-Score	P-Value		Chi-Square	P-Value
-----	-------	-------	-----	-------	-------		----------	-------
12.585	6.986	0.000	15.367	4.534	0.000		69.354	0.000

Correlation Matrix

	LX(1,1)	LX(2,1)	LX(3,1)	LX(4,1)	LX(4,2)	LX(5,2)	LX(6,2)
LX(1,1)	1.000						
LX(2,1)	0.196	1.000					
LX(3,1)	-0.136	0.218	1.000				
LX(4,1)	0.106	-0.016	-0.150	1.000			
LX(4,2)	-0.072	0.038	0.159	-0.987	1.000		
LX(5,2)	0.223	-0.097	0.114	0.160	-0.128	1.000	
LX(6,2)	-0.092	-0.053	0.138	0.330	-0.317	0.426	1.000

Means

LX(1,1)	LX(2,1)	LX(3,1)	LX(4,1)	LX(4,2)	LX(5,2)	LX(6,2)
0.527	0.395	0.428	0.060	0.700	0.589	0.661

Standard Deviations

LX(1,1)	LX(2,1)	LX(3,1)	LX(4,1)	LX(4,2)	LX(5,2)	LX(6,2)
0.089	0.101	0.077	0.376	0.377	0.074	0.074

The standard deviations are the standard errors of factor loadings that one should expect with this procedure for samples of size 148. It is seen that most loadings can be estimated with reasonable precision by the combination of a TM matrix and the ML method, except LX(4,1) and LX(4,2), which have much higher standard errors and much higher kurtoses than the other loadings. Normality is also rejected for these loadings. The histograms given in the output file reveal that the loadings LX(4,1) and LX(4,2) have more outliers than the other loadings. It seems that they are more severely affected by odd samples. Note also that the correlations of the factor loadings are generally small except for LX(4,1) and LX(4,2) which are almost perfectly linearly related. It is clear that with this method and this small sample size, these two loadings are not separately estimable.

C.3 Monte Carlo experiments

Monte Carlo experiments can be done in a similar way as bootstrapping. The difference is that there is no raw data to start with. However, raw data can be generated directly with PRELIS, and covariance or correlation matrices can be computed directly *without saving or storing the raw data*.

The key elements here are the two random variables NRAND and URAND. NRAND generates a random normal variable with mean zero and variance one. URAND generates a uniform random variable over the interval (0,1). Each time NRAND or URAND is specified in the input file, a new random normal variable independent of previously generated variables, is generated. Although we use captalized names for NRAND and URAND here, PRELIS recognizes any combination of upper case and lower case characters in these names.

In PRELIS, the random variables NRAND and URAND act as ordinary variables, except they are not read from a raw data file. Using the PRELIS command NE (for new variable), they can be combined with other variables which have been read from a file or have been generated previously. As the following examples demonstrate, there are almost unlimited possibilities of generating normal and non-normal variables with specified properties. Using the PRELIS RE (recode) command one can also generate discrete variables (ordinal or categorical). We give four typical examples. The last of these is given in full detail.

Generating variables with a specified covariance matrix

Monte Carlo example 1

Suppose the population covariance matrix Σ is given, say,

$$\Sigma = \begin{pmatrix} 1.000 & & & & & \\ 0.378 & 1.000 & & & & \\ 0.720 & 0.336 & 1.000 & & & \\ 0.324 & 0.420 & 0.288 & 1.000 & & \\ 0.270 & 0.350 & 0.240 & 0.300 & 1.000 & \\ 0.270 & 0.126 & 0.240 & 0.108 & 0.090 & 1.000 \end{pmatrix}$$

Although this is a correlation matrix, it is treated here as a covariance matrix.

The population covariance matrix Σ may or may not be specified such that a particular model fits this matrix exactly. In the first case, the *central* case, one can study how parameter estimates and other quantities behave when the model holds exactly in the population. In the second case, the *non-central* case, one can study the behavior when the model does not hold or holds only approximately in the population.

If Σ is positive definite, there exists a lower triagular matrix $\mathbf{T}$, such that $\Sigma = \mathbf{T}\mathbf{T}'$. The matrix $\mathbf{T}$ can be computed by LISREL using the following input file.

```
! Fitting TT' to Sigma
DA NI=6 NO=100000; CM=SIGMA; MO NX=6 NK=6 PH=ID TD=ZE
PA LX
1 0 0 0 0 0
1 1 0 0 0 0
1 1 1 0 0 0
1 1 1 1 0 0
1 1 1 1 1 0
1 1 1 1 1 1
MA LX
1 0 0 0 0 0
1 1 0 0 0 0
1 1 1 0 0 0
1 1 1 1 0 0
1 1 1 1 1 0
1 1 1 1 1 1
OU ND=6
```

Here we assume that Σ is in file SIGMA. We use ML to fit $\mathbf{T}\mathbf{T}'$ to Σ, but any fit function in LISREL will do. The sample size on the DA command is arbitrary, but something larger than zero must be specified. Just make sure "the model" fits perfectly. All residuals and chi-square must be zero. The matrix $\mathbf{T}$ is given as LAMBDA-X in the output file:

1.000000	- -	- -	- -	- -	- -
.378000	.925806	- -	- -	- -	- -
.720000	.068956	.690540	- -	- -	- -
.324000	.321372	.047151	.888550	- -	- -
.270000	.267810	.039292	.140229	.913329	- -
.270000	.025858	.063453	.010374	.006818	.960339

Generating normal variables

The following PRELIS input file (SIMEX11.PR2) generates 200 independent cases of six variables having a multivariate normal distribution with zero mean vector and covariance matrix Σ. Note that there is no NI value specified on the DA command.

```
! Generating Multivariate Normal Variables with a Specified Covariance
Matrix
DA NO=200
NE V1=NRAND
NE V2=NRAND
NE V3=NRAND
NE V4=NRAND
NE V5=NRAND
NE V6=NRAND
NE X1=V1
NE X2=.378*V1+.925806*V2
NE X3=.72*V1+.068956*V2+.690540*V3
NE X4=.324*V1+.321372*V2+.047151*V3+.88855*V4
NE X5=.27*V1+.26781*V2+.039292*V3+.140229*V4+.913329*V5
NE X6=.27*V1+.025858*V2+.063453*V3+.010374*V4+.006818*V5+.960339*V6
CO ALL
SD V1-V6
OU RA=RAWDATA WI=7 ND=3 XM IX=123456
```

Here we generate data on V1 through V6 which are independent and normally distributed with mean zero and variance one. V1 through V6 are then transformed linearly to X1 through X6 using the **T** matrix. After X1 through X6 have been defined, V1 through V6 can be deleted. This is done with the SD command.

The raw data is obtained in the file RAWDATA in the format 6F7.3. WI=7 defines the width of each field and ND=3 defines the number of decimals for the data in the file RAWDATA.

Now, suppose we are not interested in the sample of raw data but only in the sample covariance matrix. Then, just replace the RA=RAWDATA specification with CM=SIMEX1.CM, see file SIMEX12.PR2. Then no raw data will be saved or stored. The covariance matrix will be computed "on the run."

Next, suppose we want to generate 400 samples of size 200 and save all the 400 sample covariance matrices. Then, just add RP=400 on the DA command, see file SIMEX13.PR2. The file SIMEX1.CM will then contain 400 sample covariance matrices. The first two replicates in SIMEX1.CM are:

```
 0.95375D+00  0.37841D+00  0.10018D+01  0.59348D+00  0.30790D+00  0.83902D+00
 0.36562D+00  0.40900D+00  0.32791D+00  0.11061D+01  0.20653D+00  0.30234D+00
 0.19845D+00  0.28648D+00  0.87716D+00  0.22175D+00 -0.78280D-02  0.14026D+00
-0.12499D-01  0.32627D-01  0.10423D+01
 0.87794D+00  0.37148D+00  0.12746D+01  0.60429D+00  0.41321D+00  0.86589D+00
 0.29965D+00  0.49782D+00  0.28989D+00  0.92703D+00  0.14368D+00  0.39918D+00
 0.15315D+00  0.26849D+00  0.98916D+00  0.30765D+00  0.17819D+00  0.25911D+00
 0.30325D-01  0.40118D-01  0.11179D+01
```

This file can be read by LISREL to estimate a model for each sample. The following input file (SIMEX14.LS8) will estimate a confirmatory factor analysis model with two correlated factors, see Jöreskog (1979), Hägglund (1982), or Jöreskog & Sörbom (1989b, p. 212).

```
! Fitting a confirmatory factor analysis model in each of 400 samples
DA NI=6 NO=200 RP=400
CM=SIMEX1.CM
MO NX=6 NK=2
FR LX(1,1) LX(2,2) LX(3,1) LX(4,2) LX(5,2) LX(6,1)
OU AD=OFF PV=SIMEX1.PV SV=SIMEX1.SV GF=SIMEX1.GF XM XO
```

There are 13 free parameters in the model. The file SIMEX1.PV contains 400 sets of 13 estimated parameters, one from each sample. The file SIMEX1.SV contains 400 sets of 13 estimated standard errors of these parameter estimates, one from each sample. The file SIMEX1.GF contains 400 sets of all the 42 fit measures that LISREL computes for each sample.[1] The information in each of these files may be studied further. Here we show how the parameter estimates in file SIMEX1.PV may be examined.

The first two sets of parameter estimates in SIMEX1.PV are:

```
  1   0   0
 0.853458D+00  0.660581D+00  0.698258D+00  0.641822D+00  0.433952D+00  0.224460D+00
 0.655037D+00  0.225359D+00  0.565433D+00  0.351457D+00  0.694165D+00  0.688845D+00
 0.991918D+00
```

---

[1] If the option XI is present on the OU command, LISREL 8 will restrict the fit measures to the degrees of freedom, chi-square, and P-value.

```
  2   0   0
0.781581D+00 0.863154D+00 0.774720D+00 0.592991D+00 0.438305D+00 0.357914D+00
0.578626D+00 0.267072D+00 0.529566D+00 0.265699D+00 0.575391D+00 0.797048D+00
0.989797D+00
```

The first number is the replication number, the second is an error indicator which is

0   if iterations have converged and the P-value for χ^2 is in the interval $.0005 \leq P \leq .9995$.

1   if iterations have not converged

2   if iterations have converged and the P-value for χ^2 is either $P < .0005$ or $P > .9995$. In this case, confidence limits for the fit statistics in file SIMEX1.GF have not been computed.

The third number is 0 if the solution is admissible; otherwise it is 1.

The following PRELIS input file (SIMEX15.PR2) analyzes the parameter estimates in file SIMEX1.PV.

```
! Analyzing the parameter estimates in SIMEX1.PV
DA NI=14
LA
IND 'LX(1,1)' 'LX(2,2)' 'LX(3,1)' 'LX(4,2)' 'LX(5,2)' 'LX(6,1)'
    'PH(1,1)' 'TD(1)' 'TD(2)' 'TD(3)' 'TD(4)' 'TD(5)' 'TD(6)'
RA=SIMEX1.PV FO;   (3X,F3.0/(6D13.6));   CO 'LX(1,1)' - 'TD(6)'
OU
```

The output file gives the following information about the sampling distribution of the parameter estimates.

```
Univariate Distributions for Ordinal Variables

W_A_R_N_I_N_G:     IND1 has only one value. Error code 219.

W_A_R_N_I_N_G:     IND2 has only one value. Error code 219.

Univariate Summary Statistics for Continuous Variables
```

Variable	Mean	St. Dev.	T-Value	Skewness	Kurtosis	Minimum	Freq.	Maximum	Freq.
LX(1,1)	0.903	0.076	238.133	0.044	-0.318	0.705	1	1.136	1
LX(2,2)	0.697	0.085	165.002	0.115	0.075	0.485	1	0.956	1
LX(3,1)	0.801	0.074	216.769	-0.159	-0.061	0.560	1	0.990	1
LX(4,2)	0.602	0.079	152.900	-0.186	0.239	0.312	1	0.839	1

LX(5,2)	0.499	0.080	124.142	-0.141	-0.039	0.233	1	0.715	1
LX(6,1)	0.299	0.072	83.195	-0.066	0.044	0.089	1	0.489	1
PH(1,1)	0.606	0.077	157.739	-0.346	0.232	0.327	1	0.796	1
TD(1)	0.181	0.091	39.972	-0.315	-0.107	-0.075	1	0.401	1
TD(2)	0.511	0.097	105.975	-0.175	0.541	0.151	1	0.814	1
TD(3)	0.356	0.078	90.724	-0.208	0.706	0.053	1	0.577	1
TD(4)	0.627	0.087	144.007	0.115	0.054	0.382	1	0.902	1
TD(5)	0.742	0.087	170.521	0.115	-0.112	0.437	1	0.968	1
TD(6)	0.901	0.095	190.136	0.419	0.454	0.667	1	1.308	1

Test of Univariate Normality for Continuous Variables

	Skewness		Kurtosis		Skewness and Kurtosis	
Variable	Z-Score	P-Value	Z-Score	P-Value	Chi-Square	P-Value
LX(1,1)	0.536	0.592	-1.385	0.166	2.206	0.332
LX(2,2)	1.207	0.227	0.479	0.632	1.686	0.430
LX(3,1)	-1.514	0.130	-0.086	0.932	2.300	0.317
LX(4,2)	-1.672	0.094	1.073	0.283	3.947	0.139
LX(5,2)	-1.394	0.163	0.010	0.992	1.944	0.378
LX(6,1)	-0.769	0.442	0.355	0.723	0.718	0.698
PH(1,1)	-2.343	0.019	1.046	0.295	6.583	0.037
TD(1)	-2.237	0.025	-0.292	0.770	5.090	0.078
TD(2)	-1.610	0.107	1.983	0.047	6.525	0.038
TD(3)	-1.789	0.074	2.406	0.016	8.987	0.011
TD(4)	1.206	0.228	0.396	0.692	1.612	0.447
TD(5)	1.211	0.226	-0.315	0.752	1.567	0.457
TD(6)	2.554	0.011	1.741	0.082	9.555	0.008

This reveals that

□ The mean of sampling distribution is close to the true population value for most parameters.

□ There are some negative parameter estimates of the error variance TD(1) (Heywood cases), see comment in Jöreskog & Sörbom (1989, p. 212).

□ The asymptotic normality approximation, which LISREL assumes when estimating standard errors of parameter estimates, may not be sufficiently close for some of the parameters.

This suggests that the sample size should be larger than 200 to avoid Heywood cases and to obtain correct standard errors.

Generating non-normal variables

There are many non-normal variables and many ways of generating them.

Monte Carlo example 2

The following example generates six variables $x_1, \ldots, x_6$ having the same population covariance matrix as in the previous example. These six variables are generated from $v_1, \ldots, v_6$, which are independent, where

v_1	is normal with mean 0 and variance 1
v_2	is chi-square with 3 degrees of freedom
v_3	is a three-point distribution with probabilities $\frac{1}{2}$, $\frac{1}{3}$, $\frac{1}{6}$ at 0, 1, and 2, respectively
v_4	is a uniform discrete distribution with probability $\frac{1}{6}$ at 1, 2, 3, \ldots, 6
v_5	is uniform over the interval (0,1)
v_6	is w^2 where w is uniform over the interval (0,1)

These variables are generated first, then they are standardized to zero mean and unit variance using the formula

$$v^* = \frac{1}{\sigma}v - \frac{\mu}{\sigma} \, ,$$

where μ and σ are the mean and standard deviation of v, and v^* replaces v. Finally, they are transformed by the same matrix $\mathbf{T}$ as before. The input file SIMEX21.PR2 is:

```
! Generating Non-Normal Variables with a Specified Covariance Matrix
DA NO=200
NE V1=NRAND
NE V2=NRAND**2+NRAND**2+NRAND**2
NE V3=URAND
RE V3 OLD=0-.5,.50001-.83333,.83334-1 NEW=0,1,2
NE V4=URAND
RE V4 OLD=0-.16666,.16667-.33333,.33334-.5 NEW=1,2,3
RE V4 OLD=.50001-.66666,.66667-.83333,.83334-.99999 NEW=4,5,6
NE V5=URAND
NE V6=URAND**2
NE V2=.408248*V2-1.224745
NE V3=1.34164*V3-.894428
NE V4=.58554*V4-2.04939
NE V5=3.4641*V5-1.73205
NE V6=3.3541*V6-1.118033
NE X1=V1
NE X2=.378*V1+.925806*V2
```

```
NE X3=.72*V1+.068956*V2+.690540*V3
NE X4=.324*V1+.321372*V2+.047151*V3+.88855*V4
NE X5=.27*V1+.26781*V2+.039292*V3+.140229*V4+.913329*V5
NE X6=.27*V1+.025858*V2+.063453*V3+.010374*V4+.006818*V5+.960339*V6
CO ALL
SD V1-V6
OU CM=SIMEX2.CM XM IX=123
```

This way of generating $x_1, \ldots, x_6$ is not ideal because they are linear combinations of $v_1, \ldots, v_6$ and it is therefore, in general, difficult to know what characteristics they have apart from first and second order moments.

Using NRAND and linear combinations of its powers up to third order and methods developed by Fleishman (1978) and Vale & Maurelli (1983), it is possible to generate variables with specified univariate skewness and kurtosis and a specified covariance matrix. This method too has a disadvantage, for — unless the sample size is huge — there will be very large random variations in sample skewnesses and kurtoses from sample to sample. A better way may be to generate the latent and error variables and then generate the observable variables according to the LISREL model. This will be considered in the next section.

Generating variables from a specified model

Suppose a LISREL model to be simulated is specified. Suppose the model is recursive. Data on the observable variables $y_1, \ldots, y_p, x_1, \ldots, x_q$ can be generated as follows

Step 1	Generate values on $\xi_1, \ldots, \xi_n$ and $\zeta_1, \ldots, \zeta_m$.
Step 2	Generate values on $\epsilon_1, \ldots, \epsilon_p$.
Step 3	Generate values on $\delta_1, \ldots, \delta_p$.
Step 4	Generate values on $\eta_1, \ldots, \eta_m$ from the structural equations in the LISREL model.
Step 5	Generate values on $y_1, \ldots, y_p$ from the measurement model for the y-variables in the LISREL model.
Step 6	Generate values on $x_1, \ldots, x_p$ from the measurement model for the x-variables in the LISREL model.

For notation and formulas, see Jöreskog & Sörbom (1989, p. 4). If the model is non-recursive, the reduced form equations must be used instead of the structural equations in Step 4. For a LISREL submodel 1, as illustrated below, only the first part of Step 1 and Steps 3 and 6 are necessary.

Monte Carlo example 3

Suppose we want to simulate the following confirmatory factor analysis model with three factors:

$$
\begin{pmatrix} x_1 \\ x_2 \\ x_3 \\ x_4 \\ x_5 \\ x_6 \end{pmatrix} = \begin{pmatrix} \lambda_1 & \lambda_2 & \lambda_3 \\ 1 & 0 & 0 \\ \lambda_4 & 0 & 0 \\ 0 & 1 & 0 \\ 0 & \lambda_5 & 0 \\ \lambda_6 & \lambda_7 & 1 \end{pmatrix} \begin{pmatrix} \xi_1 \\ \xi_2 \\ \xi_3 \end{pmatrix} + \begin{pmatrix} \delta_1 \\ \delta_2 \\ \delta_3 \\ \delta_4 \\ \delta_5 \\ \delta_6 \end{pmatrix} ,
$$

where the covariance matrix of (ξ_1, ξ_2, ξ_3) is

$$
\Phi = \begin{pmatrix} \phi_{11} & & \\ \phi_{21} & \phi_{22} & \\ 0 & 0 & \phi_{33} \end{pmatrix} ,
$$

and the covariance matrix of $(\delta_1, \delta_2, \delta_3, \delta_4, \delta_5, \delta_6)$ is

$$
\Theta_\delta = \text{diag}\,(\theta_1, \theta_2, \theta_3, \theta_4, \theta_5, \theta_6) \, .
$$

We assume that

- ξ_1, ξ_2 and ξ_3 are trivariate normal with zero means
- δ_i is uniformly distributed over the interval $(0, \theta_i)$, where $i = 1, \ldots, 6$
- δ_i is independent of δ_j for $i \neq j$
- δ_i is independent of ξ_j for $i = 1, \ldots, 6$ and $j = 1, 2, 3$

and that the parameter values are

$$
(\lambda_1, \lambda_2, \lambda_3, \lambda_4, \lambda_5, \lambda_6, \lambda_7) = (.2, .4, .7, .7, .8, .2, .3) \, ,
$$

$$
(\phi_{11}, \phi_{21}, \phi_{22}, \phi_{33}) = (.64, .5, .65, .81) \, ,
$$

$$
(\theta_1, \theta_2, \theta_3, \theta_4, \theta_5, \theta_6) = (2, 2.5, 3, 3.5, 4, 4.5) \, .
$$

Then data on the observed x-variables can be generated by the following PRELIS input file (SIMEX31.PR2):

```
! Generating Sample Covariance Matrix for Confirmatory Factor Analysis Model
DA NO=200
CO ALL
NE KSI1=.7*NRAND; NE KSI2=.5*KSI1+.7*NRAND; NE KSI3=.9*NRAND
NE DELTA1=2*URAND
NE DELTA2=2.5*URAND
NE DELTA3=3*URAND
NE DELTA4=3.5*URAND
NE DELTA5=4*URAND
NE DELTA6=4.5*URAND
NE X1=.2*KSI1+.4*KSI2+.7*KSI3+DELTA1
NE X2=KSI1+DELTA2
NE X3=.7*KSI1+DELTA3
NE X4=KSI2+DELTA4
NE X5=.8*KSI2+DELTA5
NE X6=.2*KSI1+.3*KSI2+KSI3+DELTA6
SD KSI1-KSI3 DELTA1-DELTA6
OU CM=SIMEX3.CM XM IX=123
```

To obtain r replicates, just add RP=r on the DA command.

Several other variations of this are possible. For example,

- one can let both ξ and δ be non-normal
- one can let some ξ-variable correlate with some δ-variable
- one can let a ξ-variable and a δ-variable be uncorrelated but functionally related

In the last two cases, fundamental assumptions of the LISREL model are violated, but it may interesting to study what happens in such cases.

Generating ordinal variables

Monte Carlo example 4

We want to study the distribution of the goodness-of-fit statistics when a specified model (the same as in the bootstrap example) is estimated by WLS on the basis of polychoric correlations for ordinal variables. To make valid conclusions we want to simulate ordinal variables which are like the empirical data in EFFICACY.RAW as much as possible.

Step 1

We begin by running PRELIS 2 on EFFICACY.RAW to estimate the marginal frequencies of each ordinal variable and the polychoric correlation matrix and its asymptotic covariance matrix.

The input file (SIMEX41.PR2) is:

```
! Computing Thresholds and PM and AC Matrices from EFFICACY.RAW
DA NI=6
LA=EFFICACY.LAB
RA=EFFICACY.RAW FO;(6F1.0)
OU MA=PM PM=EFFICACY.PML AC=EFFICACY.ACP TH=EFFICACY.TH
```

The output file gives the following proportions for the univariate marginal distributions:

```
   NOSAY    .064 .532 .293 .111
  VOTING    .030 .327 .461 .182
 COMPLEX    .040 .172 .532 .256
  NOCARE    .034 .401 .424 .141
   TOUCH    .017 .276 .542 .165
INTEREST    .024 .340 .484 .152
```

These marginal distributions correspond to the following thresholds also given in the output file:

```
THRESHOLDS FOR ORDINAL VARIABLES :

   NOSAY   -1.522    0.243    1.221
  VOTING   -1.876   -0.367    0.908
 COMPLEX   -1.746   -0.799    0.656
  NOCARE   -1.829   -0.165    1.074
   TOUCH   -2.124   -0.545    0.974
INTEREST   -1.985   -0.349    1.030
```

The thresholds are also saved in the file EFFICACY.TH.

Step 2

Next, we fit the model to the matrix of polychoric correlations with the WLS method. Thus, run LISREL 8 with the following command file (SIMEX42.LS8):

```
! Computing and Saving Sigma for Measurement Model
DA NI=6 NO=297 MA=PM
LA=EFFICACY.LAB
PM=EFFICACY.PML
AC=EFFICACY.ACP
MO NX=6 NK=2 PH=ST
FR LX(1,1) LX(2,1) LX(3,1) LX(4,1) LX(4,2) LX(5,2) LX(6,2)
OU SI=EFFICACY.SIG
```

The fitted covariance matrix in file EFFICACY.SIG will be used together with the proportions obtained in Step 1 to generate the random data in the next step. Since the factor loadings obtained in this run fit the correlation matrix in file EFFICACY.SIG perfectly, this means that the model we will simulate holds exactly in the population. It is also possible to generate data from a population in which the investigated model does not hold exactly but only approximately. For this purpose, use the sample correlation matrix EFFICACY.PML obtained in Step 1 instead of EFFICACY.SIG in what follows.

Step 3

To generate ordinal variables with the marginal distributions obtained in Step 1, we need a lower triangular matrix T that factorizes the matrix in EFFICACY.SIG. This is obtained as in Monte Carlo Example 1. The matrix T is:

```
1.000000    - -       - -       - -       - -       - -
 .311390    .950282   - -       - -       - -       - -
 .376890    .173843   .909798   - -       - -       - -
 .490220    .226112   .242650   .806026   - -       - -
 .379350    .174984   .187775   .475599   .751013   - -
 .417710    .192668   .206755   .523676   .204797   .655341
```

We can then generate the ordinal variables and their polychoric correlations for each sample without actually storing the raw data. We can also obtain the estimated asymptotic covariance matrix of the polychoric correlations for each sample. All this is done by running the following PRELIS input file (SIMEX43.LS8):

```
! Estimating 200 polychoric correlation matrices from Monte Carlo data
DA NO=400 RP=200
NE V1=NRAND
NE V2=NRAND
NE V3=NRAND
NE V4=NRAND
NE V5=NRAND
NE V6=NRAND

NE X1=V1
NE X2=.311390*V1+.950282*V2
NE X3=.376890*V1+.173843*V2+.909798*V3
NE X4=.490220*V1+.226112*V2+.242650*V3+.806026*V4
NE X5=.379350*V1+.174984*V2+.187775*V3+.475599*V4+.751013*V5
NE X6=.417710*V1+.192668*V2+.206755*V3+.523676*V4+.204797*V5+.655341*V6

RE X1 OLD=-20-1.522,-1.522- .243, .243-1.221,1.221-20 NEW=1,2,3,4
RE X2 OLD=-20-1.876,-1.876-.367,-.367- .908, .908-20 NEW=1,2,3,4
RE X3 OLD=-20-1.746,-1.746-.799,-.799- .656, .656-20 NEW=1,2,3,4
RE X4 OLD=-20-1.829,-1.829-.165,-.165-1.074,1.074-20 NEW=1,2,3,4
RE X5 OLD=-20-2.124,-2.124-.545,-.545- .974, .974-20 NEW=1,2,3,4
RE X6 OLD=-20-1.985,-1.985-.349,-.349-1.030,1.030-20 NEW=1,2,3,4
SD V1-V6
OU IX=2345 MA=PM PM=EFFICACY.PMM AC=EFFICACY.ACM XB XT
```

The first part of this input generates independent random normal deviates. The second part transforms these, using the **T** matrix, to a set of multinormal variables with covariance matrix EFFICACY.SIG. Finally, in the last part, these multinormal variables are ordinalized by grouping them in intervals according to the thresholds in EFFICACY.TH.

After this run, we have 200 matrices of polychoric correlations in file EFFICACY.PMM and 200 corresponding asymptotic covariance matrices in file EFFICACY.ACM.

Alternatively, we could use the fitted solution from Step 2 to generate $\xi_1, \xi_2, \delta_1, \ldots, \delta_6$ first and then the underlying x-variables as linear combinations of these according to the model, as in Monte Carlo Example 3. The ordinalization remains the same. We leave it to the reader to write the input file for this alternative.

Step 4

Each of these matrices will now be analyzed by fitting a LISREL model to the polychoric correlations by WLS. For each sample analyzed, all the goodness-of-fit measures will be saved in the file EFFICACY.GFM. The input file (SIMEX44.LS8) for LISREL 8 is:

```
! Generating 200 Sets of Fit Measures from EFFICACY.PMM and EFFICACY.ACM
DA NI=6 NO=400 MA=PM RP=200
LA=EFFICACY.LAB REWIND
PM=EFFICACY.PMM
AC=EFFICACY.ACM
MO NX=6 NK=2 PH=ST
FR LX(1,1) LX(2,1) LX(3,1) LX(4,1) LX(4,2) LX(5,2) LX(6,2)
OU GF=EFFICACY.GFM XO
```

The fit measures for the first Monte Carlo sample look like this:

```
1   0   0    7  0.57590D+01  0.56816D+00  0.12523D+02  0.84628D-01  0.92959D+00
0.99589D+00  0.12087D+01  0.99072D+00  0.00000D+00  0.00000D+00  0.83115D+01
0.14434D-01  0.00000D+00  0.00000D+00  0.20831D-01  0.00000D+00  0.00000D+00
0.54551D-01  0.92732D+00  0.87719D-01  0.87719D-01  0.10855D+00  0.10526D+00
0.75115D+01  0.29851D+04  0.29971D+04  0.33759D+02  0.42000D+02  0.30271D+04
0.10364D+03  0.14682D+03  0.18544D-01  0.18544D-01  0.99834D+00  0.99501D+00
0.33278D+00  0.99807D+00  0.10009D+01  0.46577D+00  0.10000D+01  0.10004D+01
0.99587D+00  0.12811D+04
```

The first number is the replication number. The next two numbers are the same error indicators as described on page 193. The fourth integer is the degrees of freedom for the model. The other numbers are all the 49 fit measures that LISREL 8 computes and they are given in exactly the same order they appear in the output file, see Jöreskog & Sörbom (1994c). For definition of the fit measures, see Jöreskog & Sörbom (1993, Chapter 4). We note that chi-square is the first fit measure, the P-value is the second, and RMSEA is the 15th[2].

---

[2]Note that the numbers following the degrees of freedom are the four chi-squares and their corresponding P-values, see Section *GF File* in Chapter 4 of Jöreskog, *et al.* (1999).

Step 5

We can now analyze the 200 sets of fit measures in the EFFICACY.GFM file. Here we study only the three measures mentioned previously. The input file (SIMEX45.PR2) for PRELIS 2 is:

```
Analyzing 200 Sets of Fit Measures in EFFICACY.GFM
DA NI=3
LA
CHI2 P RMSEA
RA=EFFICACY.GFM FO;(16X,2D13.5//52X,D13.5/////)
CO ALL
OU MA=KM WP
```

The following results are obtained.

Univariate Summary Statistics for Continuous Variables

Variable	Mean	St. Dev.	T-Value	Skewness	Kurtosis	Minimum	Freq.	Maximum	Freq.
CHI2	7.457	4.131	25.525	1.496	4.179	0.678	1	29.279	1
P	0.470	0.288	23.025	0.110	-1.184	0.000	1	0.998	1
RMSEA	0.015	0.020	10.898	1.077	0.324	0.000	109	0.089	1

Test of Univariate Normality for Continuous Variables

Variable	Skewness Z-Score	P-Value	Kurtosis Z-Score	P-Value	Skewness and Kurtosis Chi-Square	P-Value
CHI2	3.474	0.001	5.058	0.000	37.650	0.000
P	0.951	0.342	-8.893	0.000	79.985	0.000
RMSEA	3.136	0.002	1.087	0.277	11.016	0.004

Test of Multivariate Normality for Continuous Variables

Value	Skewness Z-Score	P-Value	Value	Kurtosis Z-Score	P-Value	Skewness and Kurtosis Chi-Square	P-Value
39.607	27.599	0.000	43.434	11.346	0.000	890.422	0.000

Correlation Matrix

	CHI2	P	RMSEA
CHI2	1.000		
P	-0.906	1.000	
RMSEA	0.942	-0.871	1.000

```
Means

                CHI2            P        RMSEA
               7.457        0.470        0.015

Standard Deviations

                CHI2            P        RMSEA
               4.131        0.288        0.020
```

With 7 degrees of freedom the theoretical mean of chi-square is 7 and the standard deviation is $\sqrt{14} = 3.742$. It is seen that the standard deviation is underestimated. All three fit measures are almost perfectly correlated. There are 108 zero values of RMSEA. This is the number of times out of 200 that chi-square is below the degrees of freedom.

The histograms in the output file show that chi-square is roughly distributed as χ^2 with 7 degrees of freedom. This can be tested by grouping the chi-square measure into 10 equally probable intervals, as done with the following input file (SIMEX46.PR2):

```
! Analyzing 200 Sets of Chi-square Measures in EFFICACY.GFM
DA NI=1
LA;CHI2
RA=EFFICACY.GFM FO;(16X,D13.5////////)
RE CHI2 OLD=0-2.83,2.8301-3.82,3.8201-4.67,4.6701-5.49 NEW=1,2,3,4
RE CHI2 OLD=5.4901-6.35,6.3501-7.28,7.2801-8.38,8.3801-9.80 NEW=5,6,7,8
RE CHI2 OLD=9.801-12.0,12.001-4711 NEW=9,10
OU
```

The output file gives the following distribution for the grouped chi-square.

```
CHI2 Frequency Percentage Bar Chart
  1      17        8.5    ****************
  2      17        8.5    ****************
  3      18        9.0    *****************
  4      19        9.5    ******************
  5      25       12.5    ************************
  6      18        9.0    *****************
  7      16        8.0    ***************
  8      27       13.5    **************************
  9      19        9.5    ******************
 10      24       12.0    ***********************
```

It is quite obvious from this that chi-square follows a χ^2 with 7 degrees of freedom rather closely. A formal chi-square test of this gives $\chi^2 = 6.7$ with 9 degrees of freedom.

APPENDIX C: SIMULATION WITH PRELIS AND LISREL

D | Syntax Overview

This section provides a convenient reference to PRELIS 2. It has been updated with the additional syntax introduced with the new statistical features in LISREL 8 (Jöreskog, *et alii*, 1999).

The commands are arranged in logical order. The diagram is constructed according to the following conventions:

- Maximum line length is 127 columns. Commands may be continued over several lines by adding a space followed by a C (for 'continue') on the current line. A keyword and its specified value should appear on the same line: start a keyword on a new line if its specified value would extend past column 127.

- Square brackets [ ] enclose optional specifications. The brackets themselves should not be coded.

- Boxes enclose alternative specifications. Only one element of the list may be entered. A **boldface** element indicates the default specification.

- Parentheses ( ) must be entered exactly as shown.

- Equals signs = are required.

- Uppercase elements are commands, keywords, keyword values, or options. They must be entered as they appear, or they may be lengthened (LABELS instead of LA, for example).

- Lowercase elements describe information to be filled in by the user.

- Use blanks to separate command names, keywords, and options.

- An exclamation mark (!) or the slash-asterisk combination (/*) may be used to indicate that everything that follows on this line is to be regarded as comments. Blank (empty) lines are accepted without the ! or /*.

- Command order is important. After optional title lines, the DA command should appear first, the OU command should be last. The LA command should be placed before any other command using named variables (instead of variable numbers). The RA command may appear anywhere.

  All other commands may be used more than once. Below, they are given in logical order. Note that PRELIS 2 processes recoding and transformation first, then selection, finally missing values. In exceptional cases, this may necessitate more than one run, each time saving the transformed raw data.

- For format statements, see page 38. No format statement means free format: the data are separated by a space, comma, and/or return character.

- An *italic* element indicates a new feature of PRELIS 2.

D.1   PRELIS syntax diagram

["title line"]
[. . .]

Data input commands

[*SY*=[filename].PSF]   *See Jöreskog, et alii (1999).*

DA NI=k[,l,m,. . .] [NO=| **0** |]   [TR=| **LI** |]
                        | number of cases | | PA |

   [MI=global missing value(s)] [*RP*=no. of repetitions]

[LA [[FI]=filename [FO]]]
[(character variable format statement)]
[variable labels]

RA [FI]=filename[,filename,filename,. . .] [FO] [RE]
⎡ (variable format statement)   ⎤
⎢ [(variable format statement)] ⎥
⎣ [. . .]   ⎦

Data manipulation commands

Scale types

[*FI* varlist]

[CA | varlist |]
    | ALL |

[CB | varlist |]
    | ALL |

[CE | varlist |]
    | ALL |

[CO | varlist |]
    | ALL |

[OR | varlist |]
    | ALL |

Recode and label categories

[RE $\boxed{\begin{array}{l}\text{varlist}\\\text{ALL}\end{array}}$ OLD=valuerange[,valuerange, . . .] NEW=value[,value,. . .]]

[*CL* $\boxed{\begin{array}{l}\text{varlist}\\\text{ALL}\end{array}}$ n_1=clab$_1$ n_2=clab$_2$ . . .]

Transformation and creation of variables

[*NE* newvar=function of old variables, *NRAND* and/or *URAND*]

[LO $\boxed{\begin{array}{l}\text{varlist}\\\text{ALL}\end{array}}$ [AL=$\boxed{\begin{array}{l}\textbf{0}\\\alpha\text{-value}\end{array}}$] [BE=$\boxed{\begin{array}{l}\textbf{1}\\\beta\text{-value}\end{array}}$]]

[PO $\boxed{\begin{array}{l}\text{varlist}\\\text{ALL}\end{array}}$ [AL=$\boxed{\begin{array}{l}\textbf{0}\\\alpha\text{-value}\end{array}}$] [BE=$\boxed{\begin{array}{l}\textbf{1}\\\beta\text{-value}\end{array}}$] [GA=$\boxed{\begin{array}{l}\textbf{1}\\\gamma\text{-value}\end{array}}$]]

Select cases and variables

[SC varlist $\boxed{\begin{array}{l}= \text{value}\\ [> \text{value}]\ [< \text{value}]\end{array}}$]

[*SC* [CASE=$\boxed{\begin{array}{l}\text{ODD}\\\text{EVEN}\end{array}}$] [> number] [< number]]

[SD varlist [$\boxed{\begin{array}{l}= \text{value}\\ [> \text{value}]\ [< \text{value}]\end{array}}$]]

[*SE* varlist]

Treatment of missing values

[*IM* (Ivarlist) (Mvarlist) [VR=$\boxed{\begin{array}{l}\textbf{.5}\\\text{value}\end{array}}$] [XN] [XL]]

[MI valuerange[,valuerange,. . .] varlist]

APPENDIX D: SYNTAX OVERVIEW

Analysis and output commands

[WE variable]

[*HT* varlist]

[*ET* varlist]

$$\begin{bmatrix} FT\text{=filename} \\ [FT \text{ varlist2}] \\ [\,\ldots\,] \end{bmatrix} \begin{array}{|l|} \hline \text{varlist1} \\ \text{ALL} \\ \hline \end{array}$$

[*MT* | varlist |]
      | ALL |

[RG | y-varlist | ON | x-varlist | [*WITH* | z-varlist |] [*RES*=newvar]]
     | ALL | | ALL | | ALL |

[*EQ* | y-varlist | = | x-varlist | [WITH | z-varlist |]]
      | ALL | | ALL | | ALL |

[*FA* [NF=number] [FS]]

[*PC* [NC=number] [PS]]

[*NS* varlist]

[*FS* filename.MSF]

OU [MA= | AM |] [| RA=filename | [| AC=filename |]]
        | CM | | SR=filename | | SA=filename |
        | KM |
        | MM |
        | OM |
        | PM |
        | *RM* |
        | *TM* |

[WI=format width] [ND=no. of decimals]

[AM=filename] [CM=filename] [KM=filename] [MM=filename]

[OM=filename] [PM=filename] [*RM*=filename] [*TM*=filename]

[SM=filename] [SV=filename] [*TH*=filename]

[*BM*=filename] [*ME*=filename] [*SD*=filename]

[*YE*=filename] [*YS*=filename]

[*BS*=no. of bootstrap samples] [*SF*=sample fraction]
[*IX*=integer starting value for the random number generator]
[PA] [PV] [WP] [XB] [XT] [*XM*] [*XO*[=number]]

References

Agresti, A. (1990)
Categorical data analysis.
New York: Wiley.

Aish, A.M., & Jöreskog, K.G. (1990)
A panel model for political efficacy and responsiveness: An application
of LISREL 7 with weighted least squares.
Quality and Quantity, 24, 405–426.

Barnes, S.H., & Kaase, M. (1979)
Political action. Mass participation in five western democracies.
Sage Publications.

Bock, R. D., & Lieberman, M. (1970).
Fitting a response model for n dichotomously scored items.
Psychometrika, **35**, 179–197.

Bollen, K.A. (1989)
Structural equations with latent variables.
New York: Wiley.

Browne, M. W. (1974).
Generalized least squares estimators in the analysis of covariance struc-
tures.
South African Statistical Journal, **8**, 1–24.
(Reprinted in D. J. Aigner & A. S. Goldberger (eds.),
Latent Variables in Socioeconomic Models.
Amsterdam: North Holland Publishing Co., 1977.)

Browne, M. W. (1982)
Covariance structures.
In D. M. Hawkins (ed.), *Topics in Applied Multivariate Analysis*
(pp. 72–141).
Cambridge: Cambridge University Press.

Browne, M. W. (1984).
Asymptotically distribution-free methods for the analysis of covariance
structures.
British Journal of Mathematical and Statistical Psychology, **37**, 62–83.

Christoffersson, A. (1975).
Factor analysis of dichotomized variables.
Psychometrika, **40**, 5–32.

D'Agostino, R.B. (1986)
Tests for the normal distribution.
Pp. 367–419 in R.B. D'Agostino & M.A. Stephens (Eds.)
Goodness-of-fit techniques.
New York: Marcel Dekker.

Finn, J. D. (1974).
A General Model for Multivariate Analysis.
New York: Holt, Reinhart, and Winston.

Fleishman, A.I. (1978)
A method for simulating non-normal distributions.
Psychometrika, **43**, 521–532.

Guttman, L. A. (1953).
Image theory for the structure of quantitative variates.
Psychometrika, **18**, 277–296.

Hägglund, G. (1982)
Factor analysis by instrumental variable methods.
Psychometrika, **47**, 209–222.

Hasselrot, T., & Lernberg, L. O. (eds.) (1980).
Tonåringen och Livet.
Vällingby, Sweden: Liber Forläg. (In Swedish)

Johnson, N. L., & Kotz, S. (1970).
Distributions in Statistics: Continuous Univariate Distributions–1.
New York: John Wiley & Sons.

Jöreskog, K.G. (1979)
Basic ideas of factor and component analysis.
In: K.G. Jöreskog & D. Sörbom: *Advances in factor analysis and structural equation models.*
Cambridge, MA: Abt Books, 5–20.

Jöreskog, K. G. (1981).
Analysis of covariance structures.
Scandinavian Journal of Statistics, **8**, 65–92.

Jöreskog, K. G. (1986).
Estimation of the polyserial correlation from summary statistics.
Research Report 86–2. University of Uppsala, Department of Statistics.

Jöreskog, K.G. (1990)
New Developments in LISREL: Analysis of ordinal variables using polychoric correlations and weighted least squares.
Quality and Quantity, **24**, 387–404.

Jöreskog, K.G. (1994)
On the estimation of polychoric correlations and their asymptotic covariance matrix.
Psychometrika, **59**(3), 381–389.

Jöreskog, K.G., & Aish, A.M. (1996)
Structural equation modeling with ordinal variables.
Book Manuscript in Preparation.

Jöreskog, K.G., & Sörbom, D. (1988)
PRELIS – A Program for Multivariate Data Screening and Data Summarization. Second Edition.
Chicago: Scientific Software International, Inc.

Jöreskog, K. G., & Sörbom, D. (1989a).
LISREL 7: User's Reference Guide.
Chicago, IL: Scientific Software International, Inc.

Jöreskog, K. G., & Sörbom, D. (1989b; 2nd edition).
LISREL 7: A Guide to the Program and Applications.
Chicago, IL: SPSS Inc.

Jöreskog, K.G., & Sörbom, D. (1993)
LISREL 8: Structural Equation Modeling with the SIMPLIS Command Language.
Chicago: Scientific Software International.

Jöreskog, K.G., & Sörbom, D. (1994a)
New features in PRELIS 2.
In: K.G. Jöreskog & D. Sörbom: *PRELIS 2: User's Reference Guide,*
1996, 3rd edition
Chicago: Scientific Software International.

Jöreskog, K.G., & Sörbom, D. (1994b)
Simulation with PRELIS 2 and LISREL 8.
In: K.G. Jöreskog & D. Sörbom: *PRELIS 2: User's Reference Guide,*
1996, 3rd edition
Chicago: Scientific Software International, Inc.

Jöreskog, K.G., & Sörbom, D. (1994c)
New features in LISREL 8.
In: K.G. Jöreskog & D. Sörbom: *LISREL 8: User's Reference Guide*
1996, 2nd edition
Chicago: Scientific Software International.

Jöreskog, K.G., & Sörbom, D. (1996)
PRELIS 2 - A guide to the program and applications.
Manuscript in Preparation.
Chicago: Scientific Software International.

Jöreskog, K.G., Sörbom, D., du Toit, S., & du Toit, M. (1999)
LISREL 8: New Statistical Features.
Chicago: Scientific Software International.

Kendall, M. G., & Stuart, A. (1963).
The Advanced Theory of Statistics, Vol. 1: Distribution Theory.
London: Charles Griffin and Company, Ltd.

Kendall, M. G., & Stuart, A. (1961).
The Advanced Theory of Statistics, Vol. 2: Inference and Relationship.
London: Charles Griffin and Company, Ltd.

Little, R.J.A., & Rubin, D.B. (1987)
Statistical analysis with missing data.
New York: Wiley.

Mardia, K. V. (1970).
Measures of multivariate skewness and kurtosis with applications.
Biometrika, **57**, 519–530.

Mardia, K.V. (1974)
Applications of some measures of multivariate skewness and kurtosis
in testing normality and robustness studies.
Sankhya, B36, 115–128.

Mardia, K.V. (1985)
Mardia's test of multinormality.
Pp. 217–221 in S. Kotz & N.L. Johnson (Eds.):
Encyclopedia of Statistical Sciences, vol. 5.
New York: Wiley.

Mardia, K.V., & Foster, K. (1983)
Omnibus tests of multinormality based on skewness and kurtosis.
Communication in Statistics, 12, 207–221.

Muthén, B. (1984).
A general structural equation model with dichotomous, ordered cate-
gorical and continuous latent variable indicators.
Psychometrika, **49**, 115–132.

Olsson, U. (1979).
Maximum likelihood estimation of the polychoric correlation coeffi-
cient.
Psychometrika, **44**, 443–460.

Rubin, D.B. (1987)
Multiple imputation for nonresponse in surveys.
New York: Wiley.

Schrage, L. (1979)
A more portable FORTRAN random number generator.
ACM Transactions on Mathematical Software, **5**, 132–138.

Tukey, J. W. (1977).
Exploratory Data Analysis.
Reading, MA: Addison-Wesley Publishing Company.

Vale, C.D., & Maurelli, V.A. (1983)
Simulating multivariate nonnormal distributions.
Psychometrika, **48**, 465–471.

Author index

Subject index

FORTRAN format, 38
Forward slash (/),
    in command file, 53
    in format statement, 39, 43
Free format, 38, 52, 56
FT (command), 87, 176, 179

GA (keyword), 70
GINV utility, 170
GLS (method), 23, 27

Heywood case, 194
Homogeneity test, 85, 173
HT (command), 85, 174

IM (command), 77, 153
Image analysis, 91
Imputation, 77, 78, 153
Interactive LISREL, 6
Ivarlist, 77, 153
IX (keyword), 94, 171, 184

Kendall's tau-c, 8, 93, 167
KM (keyword), 93, 158
KM (keyword value), 7, 21, 92
Kurtosis test, 166

LA (command), 51
Labels, for categories, 65
LI (keyword value), 48
Likert scale, 4, 18
Line continuation, 205
Line length, 205
Listwise deletion, 25, 152
LO (command), 70

MA (keyword), 92
Marginal probability, 13
Marginal threshold, 89
Matrix
    asymptotic (co)variance, 25, 167
    augmented moment, 96, 169
    data, 18
    weight, 25, 170
MC (keyword), 49, 147
ME (keyword), 93, 171
Merging files, 163
MI (command), 80
MI (keyword), 49, 152
Missing value, 77, 80, 152, 165, 185
ML (method), 15, 23, 27
MM (keyword), 93, 158
MM (keyword value), 20, 92
Monte Carlo,
    sampling, 183
    study, 8
Moore-Penrose generalized inverse, 169
MS (keyword), 171
MT (command), 89, 179
Mvarlist, 77, 153

ND (keyword), 94, 191
NE (command), 67, 160
NEW (keyword), 62
New variable, 67, 160
NI (keyword), 48
NO (keyword), 48
Normal scores, 5, 7, 21
Normal theory, 23
Normality assumption, 4

NRAND variable, 67, 189

OLD (keyword), 62
OM (keyword), 93, 158
OM (keyword value), 7, 22, 25, 92
ON (specification), 90
Optimal scores, 7, 23, 92, 96
Optional command, 45
OR (command), 49, 59
Order of commands, 35, 45, 206
Order of computations, 36, 164
Ordinal variable, 4, 37, 146
OU (command), 92

PA (keyword value), 48
PA (option), 94
Pairwise deletion, 19
Panel study, 176
Parenthesis, in command file, 39
Pearson correlations, 7
Physical line, 35
PM (keyword), 93, 158
PM (keyword value), 7, 22, 25, 92
PO (command), 70
Polychoric correlation, 7, 8, 22, 24
Polyserial correlation, 23, 24
Positive-definite, 23
PRELIS 2, 5
PRELIS system file, 44
Probit regression, 179
Product-moment correlation, 7, 8, 22
PSF file, 44
PV (keyword), 184
PV (option), 94

RA (command), 55
RA (keyword), 93, 159
Random generator, 94, 184
Rank correlation, 8
RE (command), 62, 151
RE (option), 56, 144
Recoding, 78, 156
    values, 48
    variables, 151
Regression, 90
Relevant characters, 32, 46
Replication number, 193
Required command, 45
Restrictions, 37
RG (command), 37, 90
RM (keyword), 93, 158
RM (keyword value), 22, 92, 167
RMSR, 15
RP (keyword), 49, 186
Rules for new variable formula, 67

SA (keyword), 93
Sample size, 15, 37, 170
SC (command), 72, 149
Scale type, 10
SD (command), 75
SD (keyword), 93, 159, 171
Seed, 184
Semicolon, in command file, 35
SF (keyword), 94, 171, 185
SIMEX11.PR2, 191
SIMEX12.PR2, 191
SIMEX13.PR2, 191
SIMEX14.LS8, 192
SIMEX15.PR2, 193
SIMEX21.PR2, 195